Contents

About this book

This book has been written for the Data Analysis module (9993) of the AQA Use of Mathematics A-level qualification (9361/2). Full details of the examination and specification can be found on the AQA website.

> http://web.aqa.org.uk/

A dedicated website for this book can be found at

> http://www.oxfordsecondary.co.uk./useofmaths

The authors are experienced teachers who have an excellent understanding of the AQA specification.

The start of each chapter introduces the main ideas to be covered and provides motivation for the material in the chapter. It contains two features.

Preparation

Identifies skills you should be able to demonstrate before you start this chapter.

Each chapter assumes that students possess some basic skills prior to starting. These may include material from earlier chapters. They are listed in the preparation box and a number of diagnostic questions are provided to test this core knowledge.

Challenge

A problem based on a real-life scenario; the investigation and solution of which is designed to rely on using the material developed in the chapter.

The challenge allows for the possibility of a 'project' based approach to covering the material. Helped by teacher mediation, you will find the techniques necessary to solve a real-life problem in the chapter.

The sections in each chapter consist of explanatory text, examples and an exercise with progressive questions designed to consolidate the material just covered. The sections may contain a number of features.

p.1 ▶ Key points are highlighted

Key words are shown in bold

p.4 Arrows in the margin give page reference to prior discussion or further development.

> Comment boxes are used to provide additional information or comment.

Example

Questions highlight important ideas or are typical questions.

- - - - - - - - - - - - - - - -

Answers show how to apply appropriate techniques and layout your workings.

Algorithm

1 Clear, step-by-step instructions on how to carry out important algorithms

Each chapter also includes an Investigation section which provides a wider context and further directions in which to explore the material covered in the chapter. Opportunities to carry out research and investigate the use of ICT are highlighted. Each investigation also includes a suggestion for a project.

Project

An idea or a scenario which is designed to allow the material covered in the chapter to be developed into an extended activity.

At A2, Use of Mathematics contains a compulsory module, USE2, consisting of two projects. It is hoped that the ideas contained in the Investigation section may provide a useful springboard for any future studies.

The end of each chapter consists of two parts: a check out and consolidation questions. Some of the questions, and their mark allocations, are taken from actual past papers.

Check out

Summarises skills you should now be able to demonstrate having completed this chapter.

Chapters 2 and 3 make use of information on data sheets which are included after the main chapters.

The book includes two realistic practice papers and their corresponding data sheets.

Answers for all questions are provided.

You are expected to use a graphical or scientific calculator, with statistical functions, in the examination. It should have the ability to calculate: mean and standard deviation (including for grouped data), the equation of a regression line, PMCC and normal distribution probabilities. A table of probabilities for a standardised normal distribution is provided in the examination and also at the end of this book.

Interpreting statistical data

| 7.58 | 92.88% | 6.95 | 62 | 6.69 | 7.28 | 9 | 4.29 | 37.89 | 1.80 |
| 8.00 | 61.69% | 2.6 | | | | | | | |

Measurements show that averaged over the globe, the surface has warmed by about 0.8°C (with an uncertainty of about ±0.2°C) since 1850.

A quarter grapefruit a day increases breast cancer risk by 30 per cent.

Violent crime figures rise by 12%

MMR – risk of brain disorders?

Most of the egg production in this country, sadly, is now affected with salmonella.

TV kills, claim scientists

The formal threshold for claiming the discovery of a particle is a 5-sigma level - equivalent to a one-in-3.5 million chance.

The full-time gender pay gap between women and men is 14.9 per cent

| 44 | 4.24 | 92.95% | 6.30 | 61 | 1.45 | 3.69 | 3 | | 977.74 | 7.39 |

Lies, damned lies, and statistics

Popularised by Mark Twain

Three hundred years ago statistics grew out of the need of governments to have information on their populations and economies in order to better administer them. Today the collection and interpretation of data has become almost ubiquitous. Businesses collect and use data to help them monitor and run their organisations. Scientists use statistics to help them decide between theories. Schools use statistics to help monitor their performance. Everywhere you look you are bombarded by statistics designed to influence your decisions. However statistics do not always have a good reputation.

In this book, you will learn how to make sense of statistics for yourself.

Data can be qualitative, in which case it is described by a name – a colour, a flavour, a nationality, etc. or it can be numerical. Numerical data is further divided into two types, discrete and continuous.

> ▶ **Discrete** data is data whose possible values can all be listed

The list will usually be finite but can, in principle, be infinite.

Examples include: the number of letters received each day; the number of people on a bus; the number of windows in your house; shoe size (which can also have half integer values); the number of cars that travel on the M25 in a given day; and the population of the UK at midnight last night.

Variables which are *not* discrete include time, height and weight and these are considered in detail in chapter **2**.

p.34 ▶

In this chapter you will learn how to characterise a data set's typical value, the amount of variation in its values and techniques for usefully displaying and comparing data sets.

Preparation

Before you start this chapter, you should be able to

- **Use your calculator competently**

1 Calculate   **a)** 356×29.01
                 b) $74.2 \div 30.19$

- **Plot points on a grid having chosen suitable scales**

2 On a grid, plot the points $(4, 3)$ and $(8.2, -7.2)$

- **Round data to a given number of significant figures or decimal places**

3   **a)** Round 3.574 to 2 decimal places
     b) Round 21.485 to 3 significant figures

Challenge

One of the most important considerations when you think about future jobs is the likely salary that you could earn.

Collect some data on wages/salaries for a number of different jobs. What is the typical salary for a given job? How much variation is there in the salaries being paid for the same job? How should you compare the salaries for different jobs?

You may also be able to find data on the salaries paid in different countries for the same job. How do these compare?

1.1 Mean, median and mode

When you have two or more different sets of data, it is very useful to be able to compare a typical measurement from one set of data with a typical measurement from a second set of data. This statistic must be representative of the distribution and is usually located at or near the centre of the distribution; this is called a **measure of central location** or **average**.

You often talk about 'averages' in the real world. For example, you might describe someone as being above average height, or a car being more expensive than average.

There are three different types of average and, with practice, you can learn which one is more appropriate to use in a given situation.

The **mean** measures the middle of a data set by adding all the data values and dividing by the number of data values. Most people assume that the mean is the 'average', although in statistics it is better to be precise and use the word 'mean'.

How to find the mean	
1 Add together all the data values 2 Divide by the number of data values	If the variable is called x, the mean is written with a bar over it, $\bar{x}$.

When all the data values are placed in ascending, or descending, order, the **median** is the middle value of the data set. So the median value of a house price in the UK is the value of the 'middle' valued house. The median is helpful in understanding the value of the 'average' house since those few houses which are very expensive, or of little value, are ignored.

How to find the median	

1 List all the data in order
2 Choose the middle data value
  If there is no middle value
  (because there are an even number
  of readings), take the mean of the two
  numbers nearest the middle
	To find the location of the median for n data values find $(n + 1) \div 2$.
	If n is odd, it gives the position of the middle value.
	If n is even, it falls between the two data values to be averaged.

The **mode** measures the most common value in a data set. This is useful if, for example, you make clothes and want to know which is the most popular dress size.

How to find the mode

1 Look for the most common data value
2 If each data value appears only once, there is no mode
3 If the two most popular data values occur equally often, there are two modes – do not average them

---

Example 1

The attendances at an art exhibition on six successive days are

117, 129, 88, 280, 173, 81

Calculate the mean daily attendance.

- -

The total of the data values is $117 + 129 + 88 + 280 + 173 + 81 = 868$
The number of data values is 6
The mean is $868 \div 6 = 144.67$

Example 2

The price of a small loaf of bread in pence in eight local shops is

85, 90, 83, 82, 77, 99, 82, 84

Calculate the median price of a loaf of bread.

- -

Placing the prices in ascending order: 77, 82, 82, 83, 84, 85, 90, 99

There are 8 values so the median is midway between the two middle values.

The median is $(83 + 84) \div 2 = 83.5$ p

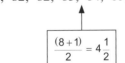

$$\frac{(8+1)}{2} = 4\frac{1}{2}$$

Note that there is no loaf of bread on sale at the median price!

Only the mode, if it exists, and the median for an odd number of data values are guaranteed to be an actual data value.

There is no 'mode' in example **1** since each value only occurs once. In example **2** the mode is 82 since this value occurs twice, which is more frequently than any other value.

Example 3

Twenty-four people are asked how much they earn per year. The amounts are given in the table.

£15289	£13246	£11291	£21290	£9812	£862185
£34312	£12102	£13890	£26185	£25105	£18102
£52153	£14356	£18001	£41085	£8329	£12106
£35206	£12987	£10982	£17185	£29015	£18102

a) Find the mean salary in this sample.
b) Find the mode salary in this sample.
c) Find the median salary.
d) Which is the more sensible of the three averages to use to understand the data and why?

---

a) mean $= \dfrac{£1332316}{24}$ The total of all the salaries

      $= £55513.17$ divided by the number of salaries.

b) mode $= £18012$ This is the only salary that is repeated, therefore it is the most common.

c) median $= \dfrac{17185+18001}{2}$ The median is the average of the twelfth and thirteenth salaries when listed in ascending order.

      $= £17593$

$$\boxed{\dfrac{n+1}{2} = \dfrac{24+1}{2} = 12\dfrac{1}{2}}$$

£8329, ... £17185, £18001, ... £862185

d) The median is a more reliable measure of the centre of this data than the mean or the mode.

The mode here simply records the fact that two people happened to have exactly the same salary, so it is not very helpful.

The mean is higher than all the other salaries except one. This is because one person is earning £862185 and this salary has distorted the mean upwords.

An 'extreme' data value, such as £862185, which is significantly larger or smaller than the other values in a data set is called an **outlier**.

In many cases data are summarised in a table. This is natural when there is a large amount of data and the same result occurs repeatedly. For example, on a given day, a lecturer in a sixth form college asks 50 students how many fast food outlets they had visited in the last week. Such data are usually recorded in a **frequency table**.

Number of fast food outlets visited	Number of students
2	8
3	17
4	21
5	3
6	1

Example 4

For the data on the number of fast food outlets visited by the 50 students shown in the table above, calculate   **a)** mean   **b)** median   **c)** mode.

- -

a) Rather than add $2 + 2 + \ldots + 2$ eight times then $3 + 3 + \ldots + 3$ seventeen times etc., it is more efficient to find 8×2, 17×3, etc. and add these results. To do this, add an extra column to the table and calculate $f \times x$, that is, the frequency (number of students) $\times$ the value (number of fast food outlets visited).

Number of fast food outlets visited, x	Number of students (frequency), f	$f \times x$
2	8	16
3	17	51
4	21	84
5	3	15
6	1	6
Totals	50	172

You may also enter the x and f values directly into your calculator to find the mean.

$$\frac{n+1}{2} = \frac{50+1}{2} = 25\frac{1}{2}$$

To find the 25th and 26th data values look at running totals

$8 < 25$
$8 < 25 \leq 8 + 17$
$25 < 26 \leq 25 + 21$

mean $= 172 \div 50 = 3.44$

b) median $= \dfrac{3+4}{2} = 3\dfrac{1}{2}$ The 25th data value is 3
The 26th data value is 4

c) mode $= 4$ The largest frequency identifies the mode.

Exercise 1.1

1   The numbers of passengers on the first twenty buses to leave a station are recorded as

    1,   4,   7,   11,   25,   13,   15,   36,   35,   34,
    31,   18,   14,   11,   23,   22,   11,   16,   17,   10

For these data, calculate the   **a)** mean   **b)** median   **c)** mode.

2   The number of cars entering a multi-storey car park was recorded hourly over a ten hour period. The data are

    75,   98,   88,   72,   56,   44,   42,   40,   22,   12

Calculate the mean number of cars entering the car park each hour.

3   A dice, marked 1, 2, 3, 4, 5 and 6, was thrown 80 times. The frequency with which each score was recorded is given in a table.

Score	1	2	3	4	5	6
Frequency	11	15	12	21	12	9

Calculate the   **a)** mean   **b)** median   **c)** mode.

4   Seven students are asked how much per hour they are paid for their part-time jobs. Their replies are

    £8.20,   £9.10,   £12,   £10.60,   £50,   £8.70,   £7.42

a) For these data, find the   **i)** mean   **ii)** mode   **iii)** median.
b) Which of these three measures is most appropriate to use as the typical hourly pay of these students?

5   The number of rooms booked per night at an hotel during a one month period are shown in the table.

Number of rooms booked	22	23	24	25	26	27
Frequency	7	8	2	9	3	2

Calculate the mean number of rooms booked per night.

6 A group of 50 students was asked by their lecturer to say how many magazines they had read during the previous week. The results are shown in the table.

Number of magazines read	0	1	2	3	4	5
Frequency	11	21	8	3	5	2

For these data, find the **a)** mean **b)** mode **c)** median.

7 An agricultural researcher counted the number of peas in each of 200 pods of a new variety of pea. The results are as shown.

Number of peas, x	Number of pods, f
3	3
4	13
5	18
6	72
7	56
8	29
9	9

Calculate the mean number of peas per pod.

8 A restaurant served a mean of 23.2 meals for the five days from Monday to Friday.
On Saturday the restaurant served 48 meals.
Calculate the mean number of meals served per day over the six days Monday to Saturday.

9 A driver made a record of the number of passengers on his tour bus.
After the first six tours, the mean number of passengers was 32.
After the first seven tours, the mean number of passengers was 35.
How many passengers were on the seventh tour?

1.2 Range and interquartile range

The averages in section **1.1** enable us to find a 'typical' value for a data set. You are interested also in how much the data is spread out – in other words, what is the difference between the largest value and the smallest value. This difference is a measure of spread called the **range**.

> **How to find the range**
> 1 List the data values in order
> 2 Range = largest value – smallest value

p.8

Although the range is a very simple measure of spread, one extreme value, like the very large salary in Example **3**, will have a major effect on its value.

An extreme value can be either very large or very small.

The **interquartile range** (abbreviated **IQR**) is a better measure of spread because it is not sensitive to the largest and smallest values of the data. The interquartile range is the range of the 'middle half' of the data and is best understood using an example.

p.6

> **How to find the interquartile range (IQR)**
> 1 List the data values in order
> 2 Find the **lower quartile** and **upper quartile**, that is, the values $\frac{1}{4}$ and $\frac{3}{4}$ of the way through the data set
> If $\frac{1}{4}$ and $\frac{3}{4}$ fall between two pairs of numbers then use the average values of these pairs
> 3 Interquartile range = upper quartile – lower quartile
>
> | The lower and upper quartiles are sometimes called the first and third quartiles. The second quartile is the median.

To find the positions of the lower and upper quartiles for n data values calculate $(n + 1) \div 4$ and $3(n + 1) \div 4$. If the resulting numbers fall between pairs of integers then use the mean of the data values in those positions to find the quartiles.

Example 5

Twenty-four people are asked how much they earn per year. The amounts are given in the table.

£15 289	£13 246	£11 291	£21 290	£9812	£862 185
£34 312	£12 102	£13 890	£26 185	£25 105	£18 102
£52 153	£14 356	£18 001	£41 085	£8329	£12 106
£35 206	£12 987	£10 982	£17 185	£29 015	£18 102

a) Find the range of this data.
b) Find the lower and upper quartiles of this data.
c) Find the interquartile range.
d) What is the advantage of using the interquartile range instead of the range in this case?

- -

The data values in order are

£8329	£9812	£10 982	£11 291	£12 102	£12 106
£12 987	£13 246	£13 890	£14 356	£15 289	£17 185
£18 001	£18 102	£18 102	£21 290	£25 105	£26 185
£29 015	£34 312	£35 206	£41 085	£52 153	£862 185

a) range = £862 185 – £8 329   highest salary – lowest salary
   = £853 856

b) The data naturally falls into four groups of six (24 ÷ 4).

   lower quartile $= \dfrac{£12\,106 + £12\,987}{2}$ mean of the 6th and 7th salaries

   $= £12\,546.50$ $\boxed{\dfrac{(24+1)}{4} = 6\frac{1}{4}}$

   upper quartile $= \dfrac{£26\,185 + £29\,015}{2}$ mean of the 18th and 19th salaries

   $= £27\,600$ $\boxed{\dfrac{3(24+1)}{4} = 18\frac{3}{4}}$

c) IQR = £27 600 – £12 546.50   upper quartile – lower quartile
   = £15 053.50

d) The interquartile range focuses on the middle half of the data set only. There is a huge difference between the highest and lowest salary, but this is only because one person is earning so much. The interquartile range does not depend on this outlier.

> If the £862 185 salary is removed from the data then the new values are:
> range = £52 153 (highest)   – £8329 (lowest)   = £43 824
>   IQR = £26 185 (18th salary) – £12 106 (6th salary) = £14 079
> The range is very sensitive to the removal of the outlier, its value drops 94.9% compared to a 6.5% drop for the IQR: the range is not robust.

Exercise 1.2

1 The numbers of passengers on the first twenty buses to leave a station are recorded as

   1, 4, 7, 11, 25, 13, 15, 36, 35, 34,

  31, 18, 14,   11, 23, 22, 11, 16, 17, 10

For these data, calculate the

a) range   **b)** lower quartile

c) upper quartile   **d)** interquartile range.

2 The number of cars entering a multi-storey car park was recorded hourly over a twelve hour period. The data are

75, 98, 88, 72, 56, 36, 29, 44, 42, 40, 22, 12

For this data, calculate the

a) range   **b)** lower quartile

c) upper quartile   **d)** interquartile range.

3 A dice, marked 1, 2, 3, 4, 5 and 6, was thrown 80 times. The frequency with which each score was recorded is given in the table.

Score	1	2	3	4	5	6
Frequency	11	15	12	21	12	9

Calculate the   **a)** range   **b)** interquartile range.

4 The number of ice creams sold by a beach vendor was recorded every half hour over a twelve hour period. The data are

18, 24, 27, 31, 43, 56, 38, 50, 43, 32, 12, 24,

32, 27, 26, 23, 18, 14,   8, 18, 16,   9,   7,   4

For this data, calculate the

a) range   **b)** lower quartile

c) upper quartile   **d)** interquartile range.

5 Zoe keeps chickens in her garden. The number of eggs she collected daily was recorded over a four week period. Thus results are shown in the table.

Number of eggs	3	4	5	6	7	8	9
Number of days	2	4	6	11	0	4	1

Calculate the   **a)** range   **b)** interquartile range.

6 The number of phone calls received by each of the twelve people in an office on one day was recorded.

16,   15,   47,   72,   61,   58,   51,   44,   45,   32,   19,   16

Calculate the   **a)** range   **b)** interquartile range.

7 The number of items of mail received by John on 36 successive days was recorded in a table.

No. of items	0	1	2	3	4	5	6	7	8
No. of days	7	5	8	4	3	2	4	1	2

Calculate the   **a)** range   **b)** interquartile range.

8 Every twenty minutes, the numbers of people passing through one turnstile into a water park were recorded.

8,   15,   32,   21,   48,   48,   48,   21,   26,   6,   6,   8,
4,   18,   32,   20,   12,   21,   30,   32,   34,   18,   11,   3

Calculate the   **a)** range   **b)** interquartile range.

c) This turnstile opened at 8 a.m. Using the data given, suggest the time when a queue formed at this turnstile.

d) Give a reason why the water park operator would have expected the tenth to thirteenth numbers to be small.

1.3 Box and whisker plots

A box and whisker plot, or diagram, is often used to compare two different sets of data. It shows the median, the upper and lower quartiles and the maximum and minimum values of a distribution.

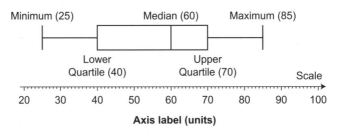

Before drawing a box and whisker plot
You need to find
1   The median value
2   The upper and lower quartiles
3   The maximum and minimum values

---

p.54 These values may also found using a cumulative frequency diagram.

For example, suppose that the numbers of passengers on 15 planes were recorded as

35, 89, 105, 111, 94, 45, 65, 78, 89, 91, 110, 101, 94, 85, 107

To draw a box and whisker diagram to represent this data, first arrange the data values in ascending (or descending) order.

35, 45, 65, 78, 85, 89, 89, 91, 94, 94, 101, 105, 107, 110, 111

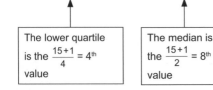

The lower quartile is the $\frac{15+1}{4} = 4^{th}$ value

The median is the $\frac{15+1}{2} = 8^{th}$ value

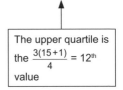

The upper quartile is the $\frac{3(15+1)}{4} = 12^{th}$ value

Minimum = 35   Lower Quartile = 78   Median = 91
Maximum = 111   Upper Quartile = 105

Draw a linear scale to cover the range from 35 to 111.
Draw a box from the lower quartile to the upper quartile as shown.

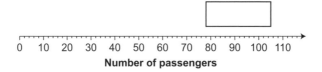

Insert a vertical line in the box at the median value.

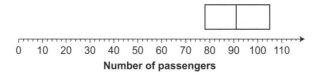

Insert two lines (or whiskers) from the centre of each end of the box to the maximum and minimum values.

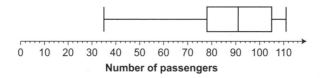

The resulting diagram is the box and whisker plot for the data.

In a box and whisker plot
► The box is drawn from the lower quartile to the upper quartile
► The median is shown as a vertical line dividing the box into two
► The whiskers are drawn from the minimum to the lower quartile and from the upper quartile to the maximum

You can use your calculator to do these calculations.

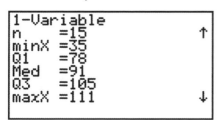

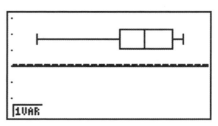

- For a **symmetric** distribution, the mean and the median coincide and the distribution is symmetric about this value

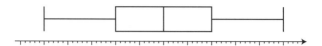

- For a **positively skewed** distribution, the median is to the left of the centre of the box

The tail on the right is longer than the tail on the left.

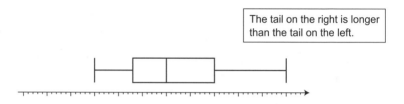

- For a **negatively skewed** distribution, the median is to the right of the centre of the box

The tail on the left is longer than the tail on the right.

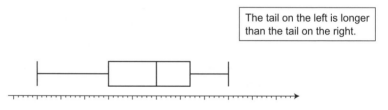

Box and whisker diagrams are often used to compare two distributions.

- To compare two distributions, you should compare their medians and their spreads

Example 6

The two box and whisker diagrams below show the distances travelled to college by students at a rural college, A, and at a city college, B.

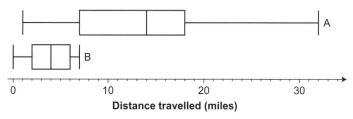

Distance travelled (miles)

Compare and contrast the two distributions.

- -

The median distances travelled by the students at the two colleges are

college A: 14 miles

and college B: 4 miles.

Thus the students at the rural college travel further on average than those at the city college.

The interquartile ranges at the two colleges are

college A: $18 - 7 = 11$ miles

and college B: $6 - 2 = 4$ miles.

Thus the distances travelled by the students at the rural college have a greater spread than those at the city college.

> The ranges are
> A: $32 - 1 = 31$
> B: $7 - 0 = 7$
> These values also show a greater variation in the distances travelled by rural students compared to city students.

Exercise 1.3

1 The box and whisker plot below summarises the daily temperatures in London at 2 p.m. during one month.

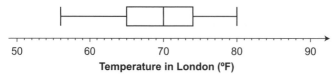

Temperature in London (°F)

Write down the
a) median temperature
b) lower quartile
c) upper quartile
d) highest temperature
e) lowest temperature.

2 a) The speeds, in miles per hour, of forty cars on a motorway between 8 a.m. and 8:30 a.m. on a weekday morning were recorded as

56, 57, 55, 48, 61, 57, 58, 59, 61, 47,
44, 62, 63, 59, 61, 64, 48, 64, 66, 63,
69, 68, 64, 62, 49, 62, 61, 49, 51, 64,
49, 66, 62, 67, 68, 69, 67, 51, 70, 71

Draw a box and whisker diagram to show these data.

b) The box and whisker plot below shows the speeds, in miles per hour, of forty cars on a motorway between 10 p.m. and 10:30 p.m.

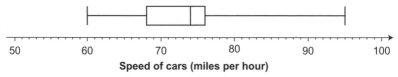

Speed of cars (miles per hour)

Compare and contrast these two distributions.

3 a) A group of 30 athletes go around a cross-country course as part of their training schedule. The first time the athletes complete the course, their times, in minutes, are

58, 65, 52, 61, 69, 49, 55, 71, 72, 58, 56, 57, 59, 70, 65,
62, 64, 59, 71, 62, 63, 58, 72, 68, 78, 64, 71, 65, 62, 74

Draw a box and whisker diagram to show these data.

b) At the end of their training schedule, the times taken, in minutes, to complete the course are

48, 52, 46, 49, 54, 82, 47, 51, 46, 52, 57, 41, 43, 47, 46,
44, 41, 39, 55, 53, 61, 54, 49, 58, 51, 49, 52, 56, 58, 49

On the same grid as used in part **a)**, draw a box and whisker plot to show this data.

c) Give two comments on the differences between the two sets of data.

4 a) At a library, visitors were asked whether they had any friends on a social network site. The first twenty people who answered 'yes' were then asked how many friends they had on the social network site. Their answers were

   9, 32,   5, 152, 249,   72,   8, 81, 42, 35,
29,   7, 82,   48, 225, 102, 17, 39, 25, 36

Draw a box and whisker plot to show these data.

b) Rachel asked the same question to twenty of her friends in her college's social area.

Many of her friends said they could only estimate the number of friends they had. The replies Rachel received were

140, 220, 170, 250, 201, 270, 194, 160, 190,   10,
300, 180, 210, 200, 260, 244, 153,   79, 121, 150

On the same grid as used in part **a)**, draw a box and whisker diagram to show these data.

c) Give two comments on the differences between the two sets of data.

5 The mean daily hours of sunshine per month in Bournemouth and in Faro (Portugal) during 2011 were

Month	Jan	Feb	Mar	Apr	May	Jun
Bournemouth	1.6	1.5	4.7	7.2	6.1	5.8
Faro	5.4	7.7	7.8	8.5	10.7	12.6

Month	Jul	Aug	Sep	Oct	Nov	Dec
Bournemouth	5.1	4.4	4.5	3.2	1.9	1.6
Faro	11.6	11.0	10.2	8.9	6.0	7.1

Source: Weather Underground!

a) On the same grid, draw two box and whisker plots to summarise these data.

b) Give two comments on the differences between the data for Bournemouth and the data for Faro.

An **ordered stem and leaf diagram** is a useful way to visualise data and, because it is ordered, it enables the median, IQR and range to be found easily.

> **To draw an ordered stem and leaf diagram**
> 1 Chose a suitable stem
> 2 Position the leaves in numerical order
> 3 Show a key
>
> *For example, the stem could be the 'tens' digit and the leaves the 'units' digit.*

Example 7

When 15 people arrived in their office one Friday morning, the numbers of emails in their inboxes were found to be

21, 17, 15, 10, 11, 28, 9, 7, 32, 21, 19, 17, 22, 6, 19

Draw an ordered stem and leaf diagram to show this data

Number of emails

3	2
2	1 1 2 8
1	0 1 5 7 7 9 9
0	6 7 9

Key 1 | 7 means 17

A stem and leaf diagram is like a horizontal bar chart. However, even though this data is grouped, no information has been lost.

You can compare two similar sets of data using a **back-to-back stem and leaf diagram**. A back-to-back stem and leaf diagram has one set of data on the left of the stem, with the second set of data on the right of the stem. Both sets of data are ordered away from the stem.

> **To draw a back-to-back stem and leaf diagram**
> 1 Chose a suitable stem
> 2 Position the leaves in numerical order
> 3 Position the two sets of data on opposite sides of the stem
> 4 Show a key

Example 8

When the same 15 people arrived in their office on the following Monday morning, the numbers of emails in their inboxes were found to be

32, 28, 21, 11, 19, 38, 32, 26, 41, 27, 29, 31, 35, 26, 39

Draw a back-to-back stem and leaf diagram to show the data for Friday and Monday.
Compare the two sets of data

Number of emails

Monday		Friday
1	4	
9 8 5 2 2 1	3	2
9 8 7 6 6 1	2	1 1 2 8
9 1	1	0 1 5 7 7 9 9
	0	6 7 9

Key   3 | 1 | 7   means 13 Monday
                               and   17 Friday

You can see from this diagram that the number of emails on Monday morning was typically greater than the number of emails on Friday.

Since the data is now positioned in order you can quickly find the range, median and interquartile range.

	Monday	Friday
Highest	41	32
Lowest	11	6
Range	30	26
Median (8th)	29	17
Upper quartile (12th)	35	21
Lower quartile (4th)	26	10
IQR	9	11

The values of the two medians support the conclusion that on average there were more emails on Monday than on Friday.

Exercise 1.4

1 The stem and leaf diagram below shows the heights of 50 students selected at random from those attending a college.

Height of students

11	7
12	
13	
14	1 5 9
15	2 4 5 5 6 6 8
16	4 6 8 8 9
17	1 3 5 6 6 8 8 8 9
18	2 3 3 4 5 6 6 7 7 7 8 9
19	1 1 1 3 3 4 5 5 7 9
20	4 7
21	2

Key   16 | 7   means 167 cm

For these students, find the
a) median height
b) height of the outlier.

2 The number of passengers on an aeroplane in the Caribbean on 14 short flights on a Tuesday and a Saturday were recorded.

Tuesday: 11, 8, 19, 7, 17, 15, 16, 18, 21, 13, 17, 8, 21, 9
Saturday: 19, 25, 31, 32, 35, 28, 29, 38, 27, 26, 21, 19, 17, 18

a) Draw a back-to-back stem and leaf diagram to show these data.
b) What conclusions can you draw from the diagram?

3 The ages of holidaymakers at a small hotel in Portugal were recorded on 1st February and on 1st August. The data found are

1st February: 45, 68, 70, 61, 54, 80, 72, 69, 73, 72, 58, 72, 64, 45, 42
1st August: 19, 27, 41, 42, 9, 14, 29, 34, 25, 29, 44, 43, 6, 17, 19

a) Draw a back-to-back stem and leaf diagram to show these data.
b) What conclusions can you draw from the diagram?

4 The table shows the ages and numbers of online sessions taken by 26 students training for a computer exam.

Age	Number of sessions	Age	Number of sessions
17	20	24	46
17	28	24	22
17	31	25	26
18	15	28	34
18	20	29	42
18	35	35	51
19	23	39	64
19	28	44	21
20	17	45	48
21	35	47	65
21	26	48	38
22	19	50	47
23	34	52	39

a) The back-to-back stem and leaf diagram below shows the number of sessions taken by students aged under 25.
Use the table to complete a copy of this back-to-back stem and leaf diagram for students aged 25 and over. (*3 marks*)

Under 25s   25 and over   Key 3 | 5 means 35 sessions

Under 25s	Stem	25 and over
	0	
9 7 5	1	
8 8 6 3 2 0 0	2	
5 5 4 1	3	
6	4	
	5	
	6	

b) Compare the number of sessions taken by the under 25s with the number taken by the 25 and over group. (*2 marks*)

1.5 Standard deviation

The spread of data can be measured using the range and interquartile range.

However, the range is very sensitive to the presence of an extreme value in the data. For example, in example **5** removing the high salary caused a significant drop in the range.

p.12 Using the interquartile range reduces the likelihood that one extreme value, an outlier, will have a major effect on your measure of spread. However, it ignores both the largest quarter and the smallest quarter of the data, which may result in important information being ignored.

The standard deviation is a measure of spread which takes into account all the data.

If you work out how much each data value differs from the mean and add up all of these differences, the answer will be zero because the sum of the positive differences will be equal to the sum of the negative differences.

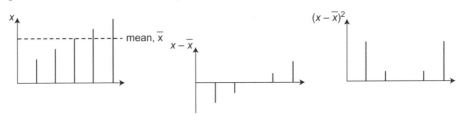

If, however, you square these differences between each data value and the mean, all of the numbers will be positive and their average will be an indication of how far the data points are from the mean. The mean of the squared differences is called the variance of the distribution. The standard deviation is the square root of the variance.

▶ The units of standard deviation are the same as the units of the data

Fortunately, in A Level Use of Mathematics, as in real life, you will not be expected to work out the standard deviation by this method. Your calculator with statistical functions will calculate the values of the mean and of the standard deviation.

▶ You should always use your calculator to find the standard deviation

To check that you can work out correctly the mean and standard deviation on your calculator, use the five numbers 5, 7, 9, 11 and 13. Following the instructions for *your* calculator you should obtain:

```
1-Variable
x̄    =9
Σx   =45
Σx²  =445
xσn  =2.82842712
xσn-1 =3.16227766
n    =5          ↓
```

mean = 9

standard deviation = 2.828

= 2.83 to 3 sf

Calculators usually have two buttons, $[\sigma_n]$ and $[\sigma_{n-1}]$ for calculating the standard deviation.

▶ In Data Analysis you should use $[\sigma_n]$

To calculate σ_n, the mean of the sum of the $(x - \bar{x})^2$ values is divided by n, whereas σ_{n-1} uses $n - 1$. The reason is that if you have to calculate $\bar{x}$ from the data itself then you effectively lose one data point.

▶ The standard deviation is a measure of the spread of the data
  • A high value means the data are very spread out
  • A low value means the data are very close together

Let the mean of the data be μ and the standard deviation be σ, then for typical data you expect

p.97

$\frac{2}{3}$ of all data to be within 1σ of μ: $\mu - \sigma < x < \mu + \sigma$

95% of all data to be within 2σ of μ: $\mu - 2\sigma < x < \mu + 2\sigma$

99.7% of all data to be within 3σ of μ: $\mu - 3\sigma < x < \mu + 3\sigma$

Example 9

Twenty-four people are asked how much they earn per year. The amounts are given in the table.

£15 289	£13 246	£11 291	£21 290	£9812	£862 185
£34 312	£12 102	£13 890	£26 185	£25 105	£18 102
£52 153	£14 356	£18 001	£41 085	£8329	£12 106
£35 206	£12 987	£10 982	£17 185	£29 015	£18 102

Find the standard deviation of this sample.

- -

```
1-Variable
x̄    =55513.1666
Σx   =1.3323E+06
Σx²  =7.5575E+11
xσn  =168547.224
xσn-1 =172172.311
n    =24         ↓
```

Using the standard deviation facility on your calculator, the standard deviation is £168 547.22

or £169 000 to 3 sf

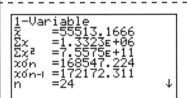

Exercise 1.5

1 The number of bottles of cola sold, each day, in a local store were recorded as

7, 3, 21, 34, 9, 16, 15, 12, 9, 18

For these data, calculate the
a) mean   **b)** standard deviation.

2 The table below shows, over two different ten-year periods, the number of days after 20 April (+) and before 20 April (−) that an oak was observed first leafing.

Year	Number of days		Year	Number of days
1951	+17		1998	−20
1952	+16		1999	−19
1953	+1		2000	−17
1954	+6		2001	−6
1955	+19		2002	−15
1956	+10		2003	−8
1957	+17		2004	−6
1958	−11		2005	−15
1959	+11		2006	0
1960	+4		2007	−17

a) The mean and the standard deviation of the number of days for the period 1951 to 1960 are 9 and 8.83 respectively. Comment on the mean value, in context.   *(2 marks)*
b) Calculate the mean and standard deviation of the number of days for the period 1998 to 2007.   *(4 marks)*
c) Compare the means and standard deviations of the number of days for the two ten-year periods.   *(3 marks)*
d) Comment upon the claim that the climate is affecting the dates when the oak first produces leaves.   *(1 mark)*
(AQA 2011)

3 An investigation was made of the effect of the distance apart that parsnip seeds were sown on the number of seeds that germinated. Equal numbers of parsnip seeds were sown in trays. The seeds in each tray were either touching each other or placed 2 cm apart. The numbers of seeds in each tray that had germinated after 10 days were recorded and are shown below.

Number of seeds that had germinated after 10 days											
Seeds touching each other						Seeds placed 2 cm apart					
8	9	9	5	5	11	14	16	16	12	15	16
13	9	12	11	8	10	10	12	13	16	12	10
7	9	9	9	8	6	15	11	15	14	13	13
12	9	11	7	8	12	11	15	14	8	13	14
10	9	9	11	6	8	19	11	12	17	9	17

a) For the seeds touching each other, calculate

   i) the mean number of seeds per tray that germinated after 10 days   *(1 mark)*

   ii) the standard deviation of the number of seeds per tray that germinated after 10 days.   *(2 marks)*

b) For the seeds that were placed 2 cm apart, the mean and standard deviation of the number of seeds that germinated after 10 days are 13.43 and 2.54 respectively.

Compare the number of seeds that germinated in these two experiments.   *(2 marks)*

      (AQA 2009)

Investigation – Interpreting statistical data

The Premier league was formed in 1992 and has gone on to dominate financially football in the UK. The cost to a club of relegation to the Championship is estimated to be around £90 million whilst finishing near the top of the table opens the door to lucrative European football. One criticism of the Premier league isthat it is becoming more predictable. During its first three seasons 8 teams finished in one of the top four positions but in the last three seasons only 5 teams finished in the top four.

Originally there were 22 teams in the league but since the 1995/6 season the number has been fixed at 20.

You can use the methods of this chapter to investigate the separation between the top and bottom of the league by looking at how the numbers of points scored in a season by the teams has changed since the 1995/96 season.

1 Find the points scored by the teams in the Premier league for two seasons since 1995/6 and calculate their
   a) range   **b)** IQR   **c)** median   **d)** mean   **e)** standard deviation
2 How should you interpret your results?
3 Why should you only compare seasons since the 1995/6 season?

Research
In todays 'wired world' many organisations hold huge data sets covering almost all aspects of our lives: education, shopping habits, whereabouts, health, etc. Data mining is the attempt to find and understand patterns in such data. What things do you think data mining could be used to do? Do you think any ethical issues are raised by data mining?

Use a spreadsheet to calculate the mean, μ, and standard deviation, σ, of a set of N data values using these formulae.

$$\mu = \frac{\sum x_i}{N} \text{ and } \sigma^2 = \frac{\sum x_i^2}{N} - \mu^2$$

	A	B	
	x_i	x_i^2	
1			
2	15289	= A2^2	
3	13246	1.754E + 08	
4	11291	1.275E + 08	
25	18012	3.244E + 08	
26	= SUM(A2:A25)	7.557E + 11	
27	mean =	SD=	
28	55513.17	=SQRT(B26/24-A28^2)	

Do your results agree with those from your calculator?

Investigate the spreadsheet's inbuilt statistical functions and graph drawing capabilities.

It is generally agreed how to find the median for a set of numbers, there is less agreement on how to define the quartiles.

4 Find other ways to define the upper and lower quartiles.

5 Does using these alternative definitions give different results from using the definition given in this book? Do your conclusions change if you have 12, 13, 14 or 15 data values?

> Can you work out which definition is used by your calculator?

Project

For a sport of your choosing, collect some data that will allow you to decide if the sport is more competitive today than it was in the past.

You will have to be sure that for the years you compare, competitors played the same number of games in a season and that the same points scoring system was being used.

Alternatively, choose a sport for which performance data is readily available. Then decide how to quantify performance during two periods and use your findings to compare them. For example you could compare

- In cricket, a side's performance in the first and second innings.
- In football, a side's results before and after Christmas.
- In golf, the players' first and second round scores.
- In athletics, countries medal counts in different Olympics.

Consolidation

Check out

You should now be able to
- Find the mean, median and mode
- Find the range and interquartile range
- Use a calculator to find the standard deviation
- Draw and interpret a box and whisker diagram
- Draw and interpret a back-to-back stem and leaf diagram

1 This table provides some information on the number of cars and vans available to the population of Yorkshire.

		South Yorkshire (mainly urban)	West Yorkshire (mainly urban)	North Yorkshire (mainly rural)
All households		530 765	854 040	237 583
Number of cars and vans	0	174 003	275 214	46 398
	1	231 838	369 148	108 038
	2	103 724	173 414	66 324
	3	16 681	28 276	12 861
	4 or more	4519	7988	3962
Total cars and vans		509 390	836 148	296 989

a) The mean number of cars and vans per household for South Yorkshire is 0.960 to 3 significant figures.
   Calculate the mean number of cars and vans per household for
   i) West Yorkshire
   ii) North Yorkshire. *(3 marks)*
b) Comment on the difference in car and van ownership between the urban and rural areas. *(1 mark)*

(AQA 2008)

2 The table below shows the hourly share price, in pence, of a retailer, Tbury, on 12 December 2012.

Time	8:00	9:00	10:00	11:00	12:00	13:00	14:00	15:00	16:00
Share price, p	13.0	12.7	12.8	12.8	12.9	13.1	13.2	13.1	13.1

a) Use the data to calculate the mean and the standard deviation of Tbury's hourly share prices. *(3 marks)*

b) The mean and standard deviation of the hourly share prices for another retailer QShop was 29.2 p and 0.119 p respectively. Compare the hourly share prices of Tbury and QShop on that day. *(3 marks)*

3 The table UK monthly rainfalls, to the nearest millimetre, for two years.

Month	Jan	Feb	Mar	Apr	May	June
2005	127	70	73	91	73	72
2006	60	65	111	68	112	42

Month	July	Aug	Sep	Oct	Nov	Dec
2005	60	85	93	143	117	81
2006	53	92	103	144	154	173

Source: The Met Office

The box and whisker plot shows the UK monthly rainfall for 2005.

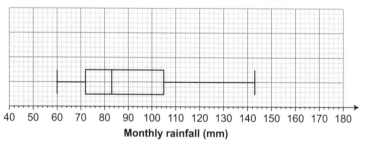

Monthly rainfall (mm)

a) Draw a box and whisker plot for the UK monthly rainfall for 2006 on a copy of the diagram. *(3 marks)*

b) Use the box and whisker plots to compare the monthly rainfall between the two years. *(2 marks)*

(AQA 2008)

2 Interpreting grouped data

In chapter **1** you studied discrete data, that is, data which can only take values from a given list. In this chapter you will study continuous data.

▶ **Continuous** data are data whose possible values correspond to a segment of the number line

Your height is an example of continuous data, as is the time it takes you to travel to school or college. A feature of continuous data is that you can never specify its value exactly. You could give your height to the nearest centimetre or even millimetre and your time to the nearest minute or perhaps even second. However, in principle, you could always make a more accurate measurement and quote ever more decimal places. The best that you can do is to say that your height or travel time lies within an interval. For example, if your height, h, is 172 cm to the nearest cm, then you can say $171.5 \leq h < 172.5$ Beware that a continuous variable may appear discrete as a consequence of the accuracy of your measurement.

In practice, when you have a lot of data, it is common to group measurements together into larger classes. For example, suppose that you measured the height of everyone in your college to the nearest centimetre. Then you may choose to group your data into classes, such as, $170 < h \le 180$ which includes all heights from strictly greater than 170 cm up to and including 180 cm.

In this chapter you will learn how to handle grouped data.

Reading tables and percentages

To obtain information from given data, it is essential that you check carefully what the data actually shows.

In example **1** it is vital that you check which region you are considering, whether the monthly or annual change is required and whether the data required is moving forward or backward in time.

Example 1

The table shows the average percentage changes in property prices monthly and annually to July 2007 for some regions in the UK.

Region	Monthly change (%)	Annual change (%)	Average price (£) in July 2007
London	1.0	15.5	342 936
North West	0.7	7.6	136 206
South East	1.1	10.5	226 242
West Midlands	−1.4	4.5	150 915

a) The average annual percentage change in property prices in England and Wales from July 2006 to July 2007 was 8.8%. The average price of a property in England and Wales in July 2006 was £166 855. Calculate the average price of a property in England and Wales in July 2007. Give your answer correct to the nearest £1000. *(2 marks)*

b) Calculate the average property price in London in July 2006. Give your answer to the nearest £1000 *(3 marks)*

c) Calculate how much the average property in the West Midlands had gone down in value during the month from June 2007 to July 2007. *(4 marks)*

(AQA 2009)

▶ Continued on next page

a) Increase = 8.8% of £166 855

$= £14\ 683.24$

New price = £166 855 + £14 683.24

$= £181\ 538.24$

$= £182\ 000$ (to the nearest £1000)

> 1.088 × 166 855
> = 181 538.24

b) For London:

Price in July 2007 = £342 936

Annual change   = 15.5%

Price in July 2007 = (100 + 15.5)% of Price in July 2006

Price in July 2006 $= \dfrac{£342\,936}{1.155}$

> 115.5% = 1.155

$= £296\ 914$

$= £297\ 000$ (to the nearest £1000)

c) For the West Midlands:

Price in July 2007 = £150 915

Monthly change   = −1.4%

Price in July 2007 = (100 − 1.4)% of Price in June 2007

Price in June 2007 $= \dfrac{£150\,915}{0.986}$

> 98.6% = 0.986

$= £153\ 057.81$

Price reduction = £153 058 − £150 915

$= £2143$

You should be able to do these calculations using your calculator.

```
(8.8÷100)×166855
               14683.24
Ans+166855
               181538.24
1.088×166855
               181538.24
▶MAT
```

```
(100+15.5)÷100
                  1.155
342936÷Ans
               296914.2857
▶MAT
```

```
(100-1.4)÷100
                  0.986
150915÷Ans
               153057.8093
Ans-150915
               2142.809331
▶MAT
```

Exercise 2.1

1 Health visitors regularly record the heights, weights and body mass index (BMI) of children.

In 2008 in one health authority, out of 2342 children recorded, 322 were over 190 cm tall and 24.1% had a BMI over 25.

a) The number of children reviewed in 2009, was 2943 of whom 411 were over 190 cm tall.

What percentage of children in 2009 were over 190 cm tall?

b) In 2010 the number of children who had a BMI over 25 was 7893. This was 25.2 % of the children recorded.

How many children were recorded in 2010?

c) In total, in the two years 2008 and 2009, calculate the percentage of children who were over 190 cm tall.

2 The UK postage rates in December 2011 and December 2012 for a standard first class and second class letter are shown in the table.

	December 2011	December 2012
First class	46p	60p
Second class	36p	50p

a) Find the total cost of sending 12 letters first class and 14 letters second class in

i) December 2011   **ii)** December 2012.

b) Calculate the percentage increase in the total cost in this annual period.

c) In 2011, the cost of sending a letter first class was increased to 46p. This was a 12.2% increase.

Calculate the cost of sending a first class letter before this increase.

3 There are 142 732 households in Northumberland as a whole. The table shows the percentages of different types of household in each area of Northumberland and in Northumberland as a whole.

	Detached house or bungalow %	Semi-detached house or bungalow %	Terrace %	Flat %	Caravan or other temporary structure %
Alnwick	30.62	32.20	27.41	9.62	0.15
Berwick-upon-Tweed	24.80	34.47	28.97	11.50	0.27
Blyth Valley	15.12	44.69	26.99	13.11	0.03
Castle Morpeth	38.10	32.80	21.98	7.01	0.10
Tynedale	33.49	31.28	26.52	8.44	0.27
Wansbeck	14.65	33.69	39.90	11.62	0.13
Northumberland as a whole	24.58	35.85	28.93	10.49	0.14

a) Explain why the percentages for Berwick-upon-Tweed do not sum to 100. *(1 mark)*

b) Calculate the number of 'detached houses or bungalows' in Northumberland as a whole. *(2 marks)*

c) There were 2990 flats in Wansbeck.
Calculate how many households there are in Wansbeck *(2 marks)*

d) Castle Morpeth has the greatest percentage of 'detached houses or bungalows'. Does this necessarily mean that Castle Morpeth has the greatest number of 'detached houses or bungalows' when compared with the other areas of Northumberland?
Give a reason for your answer. *(2 marks)*

(AQA 2011)

2.2 Grouped data and averages

When continuous data are given in groups, it is impossible to determine the actual values of any of the data.

In example **2**, you are not given the exact weight of any of the 200 students. You are only given which class they lie within. For example, within the class $90 < w \le 100$ you know that there are ten students but you do not know any of their individual weights. They could all weigh 90.0001 kg or they could all weigh 100 kg. However it is more reasonable to expect that they are spread across the interval.

If the weights are randomly spread across the interval then their mean will be near the centre of the range. By assuming that all of the students' weights are at the middle of the range, 95 kg, you should obtain a reasonable estimate of the sum of their individual weights using

frequency × mid-interval

Here the exact total weight is
90.8 + 91.2 + 92.3 + 92.9 + 94.2 +
96.0 + 96.8 + 98.3 + 98.3 + 99.5 = 950.3
Whilst the estimate is 10 × 95 = 950

The sum of the estimates for the total weight of students in each class can then be used to find an approximate value for the mean using

$$\text{mean weight} \approx \frac{\text{estimated total weight of the students}}{\text{total number of the students}}$$

▶ For grouped data you can only estimate the mean

How to find the mean of grouped data
1 Find the mid-interval, x
2 Multiply the frequency, f, by the mid interval, $f \times x$
3 Divide the total of $f \times x$ by the total of f

Likewise you cannot identify the mode for grouped data, however, you can identify the most common, or modal, class.

▶ The **modal class** is the class interval with the largest frequency

Example 2

The weights of 200 female students were found; the data are given in the table on the left.

Weight w (kg)	Number of students f	Mid-interval x	Mid interval × frequency f × x
$0 < w \leq 40$	1	20	20
$40 < w \leq 50$	10	45	450
$50 < w \leq 60$	43	55	2365
$60 < w \leq 70$	54	65	3510
$70 < w \leq 75$	21	72.5	1522.5
$75 < w \leq 80$	18	77.5	1395
$80 < w \leq 90$	28	85	2380
$90 < w \leq 100$	18	95	1710
$100 < w \leq 140$	7	120	840
Total	200	**Total**	14192.5

a) Calculate an estimate of the mean weight of the students.

b) Find the modal class of the distribution.

- -

a) Add two extra columns to the table; shown on the right.

Fill the first column with the mid interval values, denoted by x, and the second column with the multiples $f \times x$.

$$\text{Estimated mean} = \frac{14\,192.5}{200}$$

$$= 71.0 \text{ kg (3 s.f.)}$$

b) $60 < w \leq 70$

> You can also use a calculator to find the mean in one go.
>
> ```
> 1-Variable
> x̄      =70.9625
> Σx     =14192.5
> Σx²    =1.0629ᴇ+06
> xσn    =16.7008186
> xσn-ı  =16.7427279
> n      =200          ↓
> ```

> You can calculate upper and lower bounds for the mean using
> Lower bound = (1 × 0   + 10 × 40 + 43 × 50 + . . . + 7 × 100) ÷ 200 = 65.85
> Upper bound = (1 × 40 + 10 × 50 + 43 × 60 + . . . + 7 × 140) ÷ 200 = 76.075
> As expected, 65.9 < 71.0 ≤ 76.1

Exercise 2.2

1 Use *Ashes series* on data sheet **2**
   a) Write down the modal class.
   b) Calculate an estimate of the mean number of runs scored per innings.

> In the interval 0–5 there are 6 possible values for the number of runs scored and the mid-interval value is 2.5. In the interval 6–10 there are 5 possible value and the mid-interval value is 8.

2 Use *Heights of men* on data sheet **2**
   a) Write down the modal class.
   b) Calculate an estimate of the mean height of the men.

3 Use *Number of passengers on a plane* on data sheet **2**
   a) Write down the modal class.
   b) Calculate an estimate of the mean number of passengers on a plane.

4 Use *Supermarket* on data sheet **2**
   a) Write down the modal class.
   b) Calculate an estimate of the mean amount spent by the 150 customers.

5 The prices paid by 100 passengers, chosen at random, on a cruise liner were found.

Cost of cruise, c (£)	Number of passengers
Under 1000	0
$1000 \leq c < 1200$	28
$1200 \leq c < 1400$	8
$1400 \leq c < 1600$	16
$1600 \leq c < 1800$	48
Over 1800	0

   a) Write down the modal class.
   b) Calculate an estimate of the mean price paid by these 100 passengers for their cruise.

6 Use *Triathlon* on data sheet **2**

   a) Write down the modal class.

   b) Calculate an estimate of the mean time taken by these 336 athletes.

7 On 12th November 2007, there were 80 planes scheduled to arrive at Terminal 2 Heathrow between 11 a.m. and 11 p.m. Of these 80 planes one plane was cancelled. The landing times were compared with the scheduled arrival times and it was found that only three planes arrived exactly on time, 43 planes were early and 33 planes were late.

   The number of minutes, to the nearest minute, that each of the 33 planes was late was recorded and the grouped data are given below.

Number of minutes late	Number of planes
1–5	9
6–10	8
11–15	3
16–20	6
21–25	3
26–30	1
31–35	2
36–40	0
41–45	0
46–50	0
51–55	1

   a) Write down the modal class.   (*1 mark*)

   b) Calculate an estimate of the mean number of minutes late.

(*5 marks*)
(AQA 2009)

2.3 Grouped data and standard deviation

p.26 In section **1.5** you learnt how the standard deviation is used as a measure of the spread of a data set and how to calculate it from a list of numbers, using a calculator.

As well as data supplied in a list, you may also encounter data given in a frequency table. You can of course convert the frequency table into a long list of numbers by repeatedly writing out the values but this is very inefficient. Instead you should enter both the values and frequencies into your calculator.

Example 3

The table shows the number of siblings for 100 students.

Number of siblings	Number of students, f
0	16
1	34
2	22
3	27
4	0
5	1

Calculate the standard deviation of the number of siblings.

- -

```
1-Variable
x̄      =1.64
Σx     =164
Σx²    =390
xσn    =1.1001818
xσn-ı  =1.10572431
n      =100        ↓
```

Using the standard deviation facility on your calculator, the standard deviation is 1.100181... or 1.10 to 3 sf

---

This calculation gives an exact result.

p.40 You may also be given continuous data in a grouped frequency table and asked to calculate their standard deviation. Just as with the estimation of the mean, you cannot find the *exact* standard deviation since you do not know the actual data values, only the ranges in which they lie. However you can *estimate* the standard deviation by assuming that each data value lies in the middle of its range.

How to find the standard deviation of a grouped data set

1 Find the mid-interval of each class, x

2 Use the frequency and mid-interval value, x, to estimate the standard deviation using your calculator, as in example **3**

▶ You should always use technology to estimate the standard deviation for grouped data

Example 4

The weights of 200 female students were found and the data are as given in the table on the left.

Weight, w (kg)	Number of students, f	Mid–interval, x
$0 < w \le 40$	1	20
$40 < w \le 50$	10	45
$50 < w \le 60$	43	55
$60 < w \le 70$	54	65
$70 < w \le 75$	21	72.5
$75 < w \le 80$	18	77.5
$80 < w \le 90$	28	85
$90 < w \le 100$	18	95
$100 < w \le 140$	7	120

Calculate an estimate of the standard deviation of the weights of the students.

- -

Add an extra column to the table, shown on the right, and fill it with the mid-interval values, x.

```
1-Variable
x̄    =70.9625
Σx   =14192.5
Σx²  =1.0629ᴇ+06
xσn  =16.7008186
xσn-1 =16.7427279
n    =200          ↓
```

Using the standard deviation facility on your calculator, the standard deviation is 16.70082…

or 16.7 to 3 sf

Exercise 2.3

1   The number of books which 100 women had read during the previous
week was found. The data are shown in the table.

Number of books	0	1	2	3	4
Number of women	28	38	21	7	6

For these women, calculate estimates of the
a) mean
b) standard deviation.

2   The length of time which 50 solicitors
spent on the first phone call
in the morning was found. The data
are shown in the table.
For these phone calls, calculate
estimates, in minutes, of the
a) mean
b) standard deviation.

Number of minutes, n	Number of solicitors
$0 \le n < 10$	28
$10 \le n < 20$	17
$20 \le n < 30$	3
$30 \le n < 40$	1
$40 \le n < 60$	1

3   A panel of 18–50 year olds
was asked if they played video
games each week. Those who
did play video games each
week were then asked how
long they spent playing video
games during a typical week
and their responses are shown
in the table.

Length of time, t minutes	Percentage of people who played video games
$0 < t \le 60$	8
$60 < t \le 120$	24
$120 < t \le 180$	32
$180 < t \le 240$	28
$240 < t \le 300$	8
Over 300	0

For the length of time spent by people who played video games each
week, calculate estimates of the
a) mean   b) standard deviation

4   Use *Heights of men* on data sheet **2**
For the heights of the 150 men, calculate estimates of the
a) mean   b) standard deviation

5 Use *Number of passengers on a plane* on data sheet **2**

For the numbers of passengers on the 120 planes, calculate estimates of the

a) mean   **b)** standard deviation

6 Use *Triathlon* on data sheet **2**

For the times taken by the 336 athletes, calculate estimates of the

a) mean   **b)** standard deviation

7 Random samples of 1000 girls and 1000 boys were taken from each age group in a city. The data for the sample of 13-year-old girls are given in the table.

Heights (cm)	Number of girls
$90 < x \leq 110$	2
$110 < x \leq 120$	1
$120 < x \leq 130$	6
$130 < x \leq 140$	14
$140 < x \leq 150$	108
$150 < x \leq 160$	438
$160 < x \leq 170$	374
$170 < x \leq 180$	54
$180 < x \leq 200$	3

a) For the heights of the sample of girls aged 13 years, use your calculator to estimate the

i) mean

ii) standard deviation.   (*4 marks*)

b) Explain why the values you have found in **a)** are estimates.   (*1 mark*)

c) Using the values in the table

Age	11 years		12 years		13 years	
	Girls	Boys	Girls	Boys	Girls	Boys
Mean (cm)	148.08	147.20	153.58	152.98		159.45
Standard deviation (cm)	9.29	9.12	9.52	9.71		11.06

i) interpret what the values of the **mean** tell you about the heights of girls and boys at ages 11, 12 and 13

ii) interpret what the values of the **standard deviation** tell you about the heights of **boys** at ages 11, 12 and 13 years.

(*5 marks*)

(AQA 2006)

2.4 Histograms

When data are grouped, it is possible to use classes with different widths. In example **2** there are classes with widths 40 kg, 10 kg and 5 kg.

p.41

If you draw a bar chart using the class width for each column's width and the frequency for its height, then it would be misleading. This is because the human eye looks at the *area* of each bar and not simply the height.

In the bar chart it appears to be less likely to have a weight in the range 70–80 kg as in the range 80–90 kg. However, whilst 28 people actually had weights in the range 80–90 kg, 21 + 18 = 39 people had weights in the range 70–80 kg. This 'dip' in the data is not apparent in the histogram.

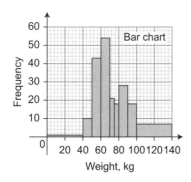

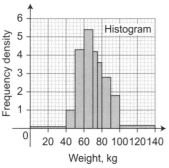

In a bar chart the frequency is shown by the height of the bar, whereas for a **histogram** the frequency is shown by the area of the bar.

> ▶ In a histogram you plot **frequency density** on the vertical axis
>
> $$\text{frequency density} = \frac{\text{frequency}}{\text{class width}}$$

The **class width** is the range of possible values in the class. By drawing a histogram you make the graph easier for people to interpret.

To draw a histogram
1 Write down the class boundaries
2 Find the class widths
3 Divide the frequency by the corresponding class width to find the frequency density
4 Plot the results

Unless the frequency of a class is zero, a histogram does not have a 'gap' between the bars.

Both the axes have linear scales.

Example 5

In the Olympic long jump event, athletes are allowed three qualification jumps to decide which athletes are to take part in the final for the event. In the Olympics in 2008, there were 41 competitors for the long jump but only 38 competitors made a jump which could be recorded.

The longest distances jumped by each of the 38 competitors in the qualification competition are given below in the table on the left.

Distance jumped, d (metres)	Number of competitors	Class width	Frequency density
d ≤ 7.3	0		
7.3 < d ≤ 7.6	5	0.3	16.7
7.6 < d ≤ 7.8	12	0.2	60
7.8 < d ≤ 8.0	12	0.2	60
8.0 < d ≤ 8.1	4	0.1	40
8.1 < d ≤ 8.2	3	0.1	30
8.2 < d ≤ 8.4	2	0.2	10
Over 8.4	0		

$7.6 - 7.3 = 0.3$
$5 \div 0.3 = 16.7$
$7.8 - 7.6 = 0.2$
$12 \div 0.2 = 60$
etc.

a) Draw a histogram to represent the data. (*5 marks*)

b) i) How many competitors jumped over 8.2 metres and so automatically qualified for the final of the long jump? (*1 mark*)

   ii) Estimate the number of competitors who jumped over 7.9 metres. (*3 marks*)

(AQA 2010)

▶ Continued on next page

a) To draw the histogram you need to calculate the frequency density. It is usual to add two more columns to the table as shown overleaf.

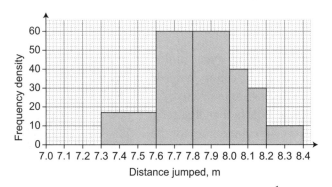

Distance jumped, m

b) i) 2

ii) $4 + 3 + 2 + \dfrac{1}{2} \times 12$
$= 15$

In the original table, only two competitors were in the interval $8.2 < d \le 8.4$ and none in the over 84 class

Include all competitors in the three intervals above 8.0. 7.9 is in the middle of $7.8 < d \le 8.0$, so assume half the competitors in this interval were over 7.9

Example 6

Zoe is a driver for a parcel delivery company.

The histogram represents the weights of the parcels which are loaded into her van.

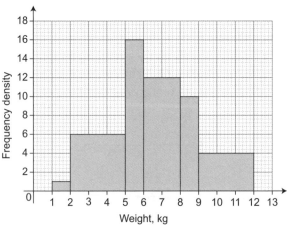

Weight, kg

▶ Continued on next page

a) How many parcels weigh between 6 kg and 8 kg?

b) Construct the relevant frequency table.

c) Calculate an estimate of the mean weight of the parcels.

d) Calculate the greatest possible total weight of the parcels in Zoe's van.

---

a) 24

b) The same technique is used to complete the frequency table.

> Frequency density × width of class interval = 12 × 2 = 24

Weight, w (kg)	Frequency, f	Mid interval, m	f × m
1 < w ≤ 2	1	1.5	1.5
2 < w ≤ 5	18	3.5	63
5 < w ≤ 6	16	5.5	88
6 < w ≤ 8	24	7	168
8 < w ≤ 9	10	8.5	85
9 < w ≤ 12	12	10.5	126
Total	81	**Total**	531.5

c) To find an estimate for the mean you need two more columns

The mean is $\dfrac{531.5}{81} = 6.56$ kg

d) The maximum possible weight of each parcel is at the maximum possible value of the class interval. The above table becomes

Weight, w (kg)	Frequency	Maximum weight	Frequency × Max weight
1 < w ≤ 2	1	2	2
2 < w ≤ 5	18	5	90
5 < w ≤ 6	16	6	96
6 < w ≤ 8	24	8	192
8 < w ≤ 9	10	9	90
9 < w ≤ 12	12	12	144
Total	81	**Total**	614

The greatest possible total weight of the parcels is 614 kg.

Exercise 2.4

1 Use *Heights of men* on data sheet **2**
   a) Draw a histogram to represent the data.
   b) i) How many men were over 190 cm in height?
   ii) Estimate the number of men whose height was less than 155 cm.

2 Use *Ashes series* on data sheet **2**
   a) Draw a histogram to represent the data.
   b) i) In how many innings were fewer than 31 runs scored?
   ii) Estimate the number in of innings in which over 65 runs were scored.
   iii) Estimate the number of innings in which under 75 runs were scored.

3 Use *Number of passengers on a plane* on data sheet **2**
   a) Draw a histogram to represent the data.
   b) i) How many planes carried more than 60 passengers?
   ii) Estimate the number of planes which carried more than 110 passengers.

4 Use *Supermarket* on data sheet **2**
   a) Draw a histogram to represent the data.
   b) i) How many of these 150 customers spent more than £50?
   ii) Estimate the number of customers who spent less than £85.

5 Use *Triathlon* on data sheet **2**
   a) Draw a histogram to represent the data.
   b) i) How many athletes spent over 3 hours completing the course?
   ii) Estimate the percentage of athletes who completed the course in less than 165 minutes.

6 At a water park, 200 visitors were asked how long they had taken travelling to the water park. The data found are shown below.

Time taken, m (minutes)	Number of visitors
$0 < m \leq 30$	0
$30 < m \leq 40$	13
$40 < m \leq 45$	38
$45 < m \leq 50$	68
$50 < m \leq 55$	45
$55 < m \leq 70$	36
$70 < m$	0

a) Draw a histogram to represent the data.

b) i) How many visitors took over 50 minutes to travel to the water park?

ii) Estimate the number of visitors who had taken over one hour to travel to the water park.

7 The weights of 90 children were recorded in 1967.

Weight, x (pounds)	Frequency
$65 \leq x < 75$	5
$75 \leq x < 85$	14
$85 \leq x < 90$	24
$90 \leq x < 95$	19
$95 \leq x < 100$	14
$100 \leq x < 110$	9
$110 \leq x < 120$	5

a) Draw a histogram to illustrate these weights.

b) Estimate the number of school children, out of the 90 measured in 1967, who weighed over 96 pounds.

2.5 Cumulative frequency diagrams

A cumulative frequency diagram is a useful method for estimating the median and quartiles of grouped data.

▶ The **cumulative frequency** is the total frequency up to a particular class boundary

As a 'running total' the cumulative frequency is most easily calculated by adding the current frequency to the previous cumulative frequency.

▶ On a graph, the cumulative frequency is always plotted against the upper class boundary

If the frequencies are given as percentages, the cumulative frequency diagram could be called a percentage cumulative frequency curve.

Example 7

p.41

For the data on the weights of the 200 female students in example **2**.

a) Draw a cumulative frequency curve to show the data.

b) Use your curve to find the
   i) median   **ii)** lower quartile
   iii) upper quartile   **iv)** interquartile range.

p.16

c) Summarise the data in a box and whisker diagram.

- -

a) The cumulative frequencies are required. It is usual to add these totals as a third column to the table.

Weight, w (kg)	Number of students, f	Cummulative frequency
$0 < w \leq 40$	1	1
$40 < w \leq 50$	10	11
$50 < w \leq 60$	43	54
$60 < w \leq 70$	54	108
$70 < w \leq 75$	21	129
$75 < w \leq 80$	18	147
$80 < w \leq 90$	28	175
$90 < w \leq 100$	18	193
$100 < w \leq 140$	7	200

$1 + 10 = 11$
$11 + 43 = 54$
$54 + 54 = 108$ etc.

Check: the final cumulative frequency should equal the total frequency, given as 200 in this question.

▶ Continued on next page

a) Each cumulative frequency is plotted at the upper bound of its class interval; the value of 129, for instance, is plotted at 75. This is because there were 129 students whose weight was 75 kg or less.

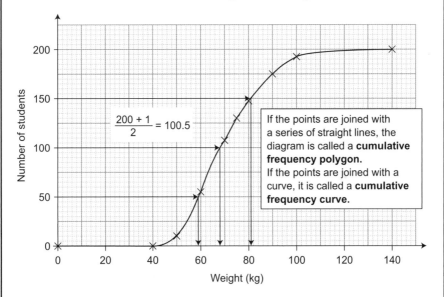

If the points are joined with a series of straight lines, the diagram is called a **cumulative frequency polygon**.
If the points are joined with a curve, it is called a **cumulative frequency curve**.

$$\frac{200 + 1}{2} = 100.5$$

b) i) 68 kg
ii) 59 kg
iii) 81 kg
iv) 81 − 59 = 22 kg

For a sample of size n, the median, lower quartile and upper quartile are estimated as the values corresponding to a cumulative frequency $\frac{n+1}{2}$, $\frac{n+1}{4}$ and $\frac{3(n+1)}{4}$ respectively.

c)

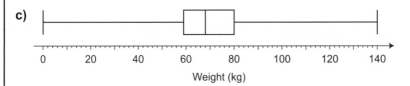

The minimum possible value is given by the lower boundary of the first non-empty class interval.

The maximum possible value is given by the upper boundary of the last non-empty class interval.

Exercise 2.5

1 Use *Heights of men* on data sheet **2**
   a) Draw a cumulative frequency curve to show the data.
   b) Use your curve to find estimates of the
   i) median   **ii)** lower quartile
   iii) upper quartile   **iv)** interquartile range.
   c) Draw a box and whisker diagram to show the data.

2 John regularly drives from Southampton to Croydon and records the time his journey takes.

Time, t (minutes)	$0 \leq t < 90$	$90 \leq t < 100$	$100 \leq t < 110$	$110 \leq t < 130$	$130 \leq t < 180$	$180 \leq t < 2$
Number of journeys	0	12	43	37	7	1

   a) Draw a cumulative frequency curve to show the data.
   b) Use your curve to find estimates of the
   i) median   **ii)** lower quartile
   iii) upper quartile   **iv)** interquartile range.
   c) Draw a box and whisker diagram to show the data.

3 Sheila has grown a large number of sunflowers. She records the height of each of the flowers.

Height, h (cm)	$0 \leq h < 100$	$100 \leq h < 120$	$120 \leq h < 130$	$130 \leq h < 150$	$150 \leq h < 170$	$170 \leq h < 2$
Number of flowers	0	15	39	41	4	1

   a) Draw a cumulative frequency curve to show the data.
   b) Use your curve to find estimates of the
   i) median   **ii)** lower quartile
   iii) upper quartile   **iv)** interquartile range.
   c) Draw a box and whisker diagram to show the data.

4 A survey found that about 30% of people who play sport have a sporting injury each year. The main cause is 'over exertion'.

The ages, in years, for females and males who, in a survey, said that they had had an injury caused by over exertion is given below.

Age	18–24	25–34	35–44	45–59	60–80
Female	19	24	41	42	34
Male	28	42	43	32	35

Remember that the age class $18 - 24$ covers everyone from age 18 up to age 25.

a) On the same grid, draw two cumulative frequency curves to show the data.

b) Use your curves to find estimates of the median age for females and the median age for males who reported a sporting injury caused by over exertion.

c) Interpret your answer in context.

5 Bev asked college students whether they had visited a social website in the last week.

The 160 students who had visited a social website were then asked how long they had spent on social websites in that week. Their responses are shown below.

Length of time, t (minutes)	Number of students
$0 < t \le 20$	0
$20 < t \le 100$	8
$100 < t \le 200$	34
$200 < t \le 300$	61
$300 < t \le 400$	37
$400 < t \le 500$	16
$500 < t \le 700$	4
Over 700	0

a) Draw a cumulative frequency curve to show the data.

b) Use your curve to find estimates of the
  i) median
  ii) lower quartile
  iii) upper quartile
  iv) interquartile range.

c) Draw a box and whisker diagram to show the data.

2.6 Percentiles

Quartiles divide a data set into four equal quarters.

▶ **Percentiles** divide the data into 100 equal parts

For example, in example **7**, the 60th percentile is the weight of the student who is heavier than 60% of the other students. The student for whom 60% of the group have a lower weight is the 120th student, that is, 60% of 200. Using the cumulative frequency diagram from example **7**, this person has a weight of 73 kg.

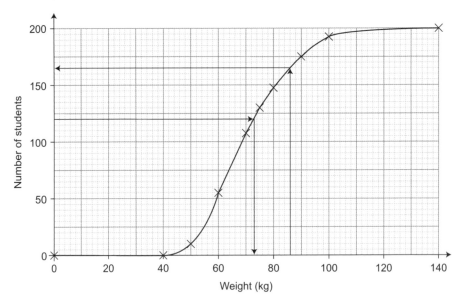

Similarly you can find the percentile of a particular weight. Suppose a student has a weight of 86 kg, what percentile does this place them in? Using the cumulative frequency curve 86 kg corresponds to 165 which is 83% of 200. The student is in the 83rd percentile, that is, 83% of students have a lower weight than her.

Exercise 2.6

1 Use *Ashes series* on data sheet **2**
   a) Draw a cumulative frequency curve to show the data.   (*4 marks*)
   b) Use your curve to find the
      i) median   (*2 marks*)   ii) lower quartile   (*1 mark*)
      iii) upper quartile   (*1 mark*)   iv) interquartile range. (*1 mark*)
   c) In one innings, a batsman made a score in the 81st percentile.
      How many runs did he make in this innings?   (*1 mark*)
   d) In the third test, Freddie Flintoff scored 74 in an innings.
      In which percentile was this innings?   (*2 marks*)
                                                                  (AQA 2011)

2 Use *Triathlon* on data sheet **2**
   a) Draw a cumulative frequency curve to show the data.   (*3 marks*)
   b) Use your cumulative frequency curve to find the
      i) median   (*2 marks*)   ii) lower quartile   (*1 mark*)
      iii) upper quartile   (*1 mark*)   iv) interquartile range.   (*1 mark*)
   c) Mark finished in the 40th percentile.
      How long did Mark take?   (*2 marks*)
   d) Kim took 2 hours and 52 minutes. In which percentile did
      he finish?   (*1 mark*)
                                                                  (AQA 2009)

3 Use *Number of passengers on a plane* on data sheet **2**
   a) Draw a cumulative frequency curve to show the data.
   b) Use your curve to find the
      i) median   ii) lower quartile
      iii) upper quartile   iv) interquartile range.
   c) A company tries to ensure that its planes are comparatively full. It
      would like its planes to be in the top 20 percentiles for the number of
      passengers. Estimate the minimum number of passengers needed on a
      plane for this requirement to be met?

4 Use *Supermarket* on data sheet **2**
   a) Draw a cumulative frequency curve to show the data.
   b) Use your curve to find the
      i) median   ii) lower quartile
      iii) upper quartile   iv) interquartile range.
   c) One customer spent £70.
      In which percentile of the customers was she?

2.7 Comparing data sets

When comparing two data sets you should comment on any differences or similarities that you find and use summary statistics to quantify your observations.

To compare distributions look at
▶ A measure of average (median or mean)
▶ A measure of spread (range, interquartile range or standard deviation)

Compare like with like, for example,
– two medians
– two means
– two IQRs

You can also comment on the shape of the data sets' distributions, for example, are they symmetric or skewed.

A pair of box and whisker diagrams provide a useful way to compare two data sets.

Example 8

At the 2012 London Olympics 85 men and 107 women finished the marathon. The table shows the times, over two hours, they took.

Time over 2 hrs	Frequency		Cumulative frequency	
(min:sec)	Men	Women	Men	Women
00:00 < $t \le$ 10:00	3	0	3	0
10:00 < $t \le$ 15:00	14	0	17	0
15:00 < $t \le$ 20:00	33	0	50	0
20:00 < $t \le$ 25:00	16	6	66	6
25:00 < $t \le$ 30:00	11	23	77	29
30:00 < $t \le$ 35:00	4	25	81	54
35:00 < $t \le$ 40:00	1	24	82	78
40:00 < $t \le$ 50:00	2	22	84	100
50:00 < $t \le$ 60:00	1	3	85	103
60:00 < $t \le$ 90:00		4		107

Compare the two distributions

Add two columns to the table, shown on the right, and fill them with the cumulative frequencies.

▶ Continued on next page

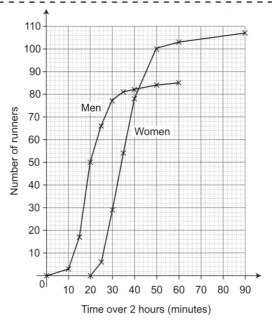

These are examples of cumulative frequency polygons.

Draw a cumulative frequency diagram and use this to calculate the quartiles. Summarise the results in a pair of box and whisker diagrams

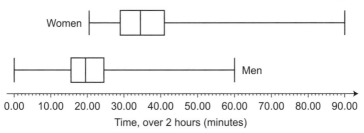

- The men are faster than the women: over half of the men have finished before the fastest women.
  (Men's median, 19.3 < Women's minimum, 20.0)

- There is less variation in the women's finish times compared to the men's finish times
  (range: 35 < 50, IQR: 8 < 11)

In the absence of any further information, use the boundaries of the first and last non-empty class intervals to estimate the maximum and minimum values.

Exercise 2.7

1 A mortgage broker records the ages of the people who are first time house buyers.
The table below shows the data for both male and female buyers, expressed as a percentage of the broker's clients.

	Age (years)				
	21–24	25–29	30–34	35–39	40–49
Female	6	24	42	26	2
Male	8	32	51	9	1

a) Explain why the percentages for males does not sum to 100.

b) Draw the percentage cumulative frequency curve for both males and females.

c) Find estimates for the median ages for both the male and female buyers and compare these values.

2 The annual salaries of 80 women and 80 men who belonged to a club were as shown in the table below.

Annual salary (£s)	Number of women	Number of men
10 000 < s ≤ 20 000	15	7
20 000 < s ≤ 30 000	23	18
30 000 < s ≤ 40 000	12	21
40 000 < s ≤ 50 000	15	13
50 000 < s ≤ 60 000	6	18
60 000 < s ≤ 70 000	9	3

a) i) Calculate an estimate of the mean annual salary paid to the female members of the club.

   ii) Calculate an estimate of the mean annual salary paid to the male members of the club.

b) i) Calculate an estimate of the standard deviation of the annual salary paid to the female members of the club.

   ii) Calculate an estimate of the standard deviation of the annual salary paid to the male members of the club.

c) Compare and contrast the mean and the standard deviation of the female and male members of the club.

3 Each year, yachts race around the Isle of Wight as part of Cowes week. In the year 2008, 1830 yachts took part and they were divided into a number of different groups, depending on the type of yacht.

In general, about 60 yachts were entered in each group.

There were 59 yachts in the 'Sunsail 37' group. The times taken by these 59 yachts to complete the race are shown in the table.

Time taken, t (minutes)	Number of yachts
$t \le 460$	0
$460 < t \le 480$	2
$480 < t \le 500$	5
$500 < t \le 520$	10
$520 < t \le 540$	22
$540 < t \le 560$	11
$560 < t \le 580$	6
$580 < t \le 600$	2
$600 < t \le 620$	1
$620 < t$	0

a) Draw a cumulative frequency curve to show the data. *(4 marks)*

b) Use your cumulative frequency curve to find

 i) the median *(2 marks)* **ii)** the lower quartile *(1 mark)*

 iii) the upper quartile *(1 mark)* **iv)** the interquartile range. *(1 mark)*

c) The times taken by the yachts in the 'IRC Division 1A' group were also recorded in this race. The data for these yachts are shown as a box and whisker diagram.

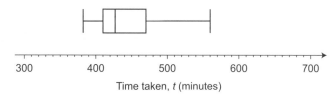

Add to a copy of the graph another box and whisker diagram representing the measures you have found in part **b)** for the 'Sunsail 37' yachts. *(3 marks)*

d) Use the box and whisker diagrams to make **two** comments about the times taken by the two different types of yacht. *(2 marks)*

(AQA 2011)

4 A survey of females' incomes, in various regions of the UK, was carried out. The table summarises the females' incomes for London and the North.

Incomes, w £	Number of females in London	Number of females in the North
$0 < w \le 2600$	7	29
$2600 < w \le 5200$	14	56
$5200 < w \le 10\,400$	25	64
$10\,400 < w \le 15\,600$	16	35
$15\,600 < w \le 20\,800$	8	25
$20\,800 < w \le 28\,600$	10	15
$28\,600 < w \le 36\,400$	4	5
$36\,400 < w \le 44\,200$	4	5

a) On a grid showing incomes going from £0 to £44.2 k and commulative frequency from 0 to 90, draw a cumulative frequency curve of the incomes of the females in London. *(3 marks)*

b) Use your graph to estimate the median and interquartile range of the incomes of the females in London. *(3 marks)*

c) The box and whisker plot of the incomes of the females from the North is plotted below.

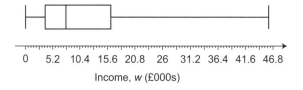

| 0 | 5.2 | 10.4 | 15.6 | 20.8 | 26 | 31.2 | 36.4 | 41.6 | 46.8 |

Income, w (£000s)

Write down **two** comparisons between the females' incomes in London and those in the North. *(3 marks)*

(AQA 2009)

5 At Stansted airport the distances flown by the first 60 aeroplanes which arrived on Monday 3 February 2003 were recorded.
The results are listed in the table below.

Number of miles, m	Number of flights
$0 < m \leq 100$	0
$100 < m \leq 200$	1
$200 < m \leq 300$	6
$300 < m \leq 400$	12
$400 < m \leq 500$	16
$500 < m \leq 600$	4
$600 < m \leq 700$	8
$700 < m \leq 800$	6
$800 < m \leq 900$	4
$900 < m \leq 1000$	1
$1000 < m \leq 1100$	2
Over 1100	0

a) Draw a cumulative frequency curve to show the data.   *(4 marks)*
b) Use your cumulative frequency curve to find
  i) median   *(2 marks)*   **ii)**   lower quartile   *(1 mark)*
  iii) upper quartile   *(1 mark)*   **iv)**   interquartile range. *(1 mark)*
c) At Gatwick airport, on the same morning, the numbers of miles flown by the first 60 aeroplanes to arrive were also recorded.
The box and whisker diagram below represents this data.
Add to a copy of the graph another box and whisker diagram representing the measures you have found in part **b)** for Stansted.

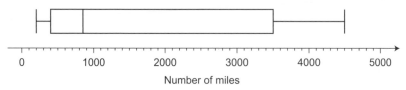

(3 marks)
d) Use the box and whisker diagrams to make **two** comments about the number of miles flown by the first 60 arrivals at the two airports.   *(3 marks)*
(AQA 2005)

Investigation – Grouped data

The diagonals of a pentagram cross in the golden ratio, φ. This means that

$$\frac{a+b}{a} = \frac{a}{b} \equiv \varphi \left(= \frac{b}{c} \right) \quad \varphi = \frac{1+\sqrt{5}}{2} = 1.61803398...$$

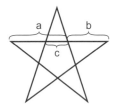

The ancient Greeks discovered this mathematical curiosity and, noticing that it appears in several other geometrical constructions, studied its properties.

Interest in φ surged in 1509 when Leonardo da Vinci's mathematics teacher, Luca Pacioli, published a book *De divina proportione*. In it he describes properties of the golden ratio and shows how it is used in great works of art and architecture. Since then, there has been an explosion of interest in the golden ratio with people claiming that it appears almost anywhere that you find pleasing proportions. Examples include in paintings and design, music, nature and in particular the human body, even down to the ratio of the pitch and width of DNA molecules.

ICT opportunity

Use a spread sheet to calculate the mean and standard deviation of the data in a frequency table using the formulae:

$$\mu = \frac{\sum x_i f_i}{\sum f_i} \quad \text{and} \quad \sigma^2 = \frac{\sum x_i^2 f_i}{\sum f_i} - \mu^2$$

Do your results agree with those from your calculator?

	A	B	C	D
1	x_i	f_i	$x_i f_i$	$x_i^2 f_i$
2	20	1	20	=A2^2*B2
3	45	20	=A3*B3	40500
4	55	43	1650	130075
10	20	7	840	100800
11		=sum(B2:B10)		1083169
12		**mean**	=C11/B11	
13		**SD**	=sqrt(D11-C12^2)	

Gustav Fechner was a pioneering German psychologist who experimentally demonstrated peoples' preference for rectangles drawn in the golden ratio.

He was also responsible for popularising the use of the median as a measure of central position and the observation that peoples' response to a stimulus depends logarithmically on the size of the stimulus, for example, sound.

1   Find out about Fechner's experiments with rectangles and his other contributions to mathematics and science.
2   What properties of the golden ratio make it interesting to mathematicians?

Research

Find examples of other quantities that are claimed to be in the golden ratio. How many of these do you think are actually in the golden ratio?

One possible place where the golden ratio appears is in the ratio of the height to the top of your head to the height to your navel.

Project

Select a sample of your friends. Record their measurements for data which *could* be in the golden ratio and discover whether their measurements are in this ratio.
Find their mean, median, and standard deviation. How many standard deviations separate the mean from the exact value of the golden ratio?

Consolidation

For a continuous distribution, you should now be able to
- Interpret data
- Find the mean, median and modal class of a grouped distribution
- Find the standard deviation of a grouped distribution
- Draw and interpret a cumulative frequency diagram
- Draw and interpret a histogram

1 The table shows the population of some European countries on 1st January 2007 and 2008.

Country	2007	2008
Austria	8 298 923	8 331 930
Germany	82 314 906	82 221 808
Greece	11 171 740	11 214 992
Italy	59 131 287	59 618 114
Poland	38 125 479	38 115 641
Portugal	10 599 095	10 617 575
Spain	44 474 631	45 283 259
U.K.	60 816 701	61 185 981

a) Which country, in the table, had the largest population on 1st January 2008?
   (1 mark)

b) Calculate the percentage increase in the population for the United Kingdom from 2007 to 2008.
   (2 marks)

c) Calculate the percentage decrease in the population for Poland from 2007 to 2008.
   (2 marks)

d) The population of Hungary was 10 045 000 in 2008. It had decreased by 0.21% from 2007 to 2008. Calculate the population of Hungary in 2007.
   (3 marks)
   (AQA 2010)

2 In a survey, chest sizes of 100 local men were measured. The data are shown below.

Chest size, c (inches)	$26 \le c < 36$	$36 \le c < 40$	$40 \le c < 44$	$44 \le c < 48$	$48 \le c < 55$
Frequency	6	34	42	12	6

For the chest sizes in the sample, calculate estimates of
a) the mean
   (2 marks)
b) the standard deviation, in inches.
   (2 marks)
   (AQA 2000)

3 A survey divides households into groups based upon weekly income. The table shows the percentage of households in each weekly income group for Yorkshire and the Humber, the South East and the United Kingdom overall.

	Yorkshire and the Humber	South East	United Kingdom
Percentage of households in each weekly income group			
up to £100	7	5	7
over £100 to £150	10	6	9
over £150 to £250	17	10	15
over £250 to £350	15	11	12
over £350 to £450	11	9	10
over £450 to £600	15	15	14
over £600 to £750	10	11	10
over £750	15	32	23
Average gross weekly income (£)			
Per household	460	657	534
Per person	198	282	225

a) Draw a percentage cumulative frequency curve for the South East. Draw the percentage cumulative frequency curve for Yorkshire and the Humber household income on the same grid. Assume that the maximum household income is £900. *(3 marks)*

b) Estimate the median household incomes for the two regions and compare them. *(3 marks)*

c) The interquartile range of the household income for Yorkshire and the Humber is £400.
   Estimate the interquartile range of household incomes for the South East.
   Compare the interquartile ranges and comment upon them in context. *(4 marks)*
   (AQA 2009)

3 Bivariate data

Sir Francis Galton, a cousin of Charles Darwin, was interested in the question of inherited characteristics. He measured and compared the sizes of the seeds of sweet pea plants with those of their parent plants and the heights of children with those of their parents. He wanted to know whether it was possible, given a value for the parent, to predict the corresponding value for the offspring. His investigations led him to develop the scatter diagram, the line of best fit and the concept of correlation. These are ideas that continue to play a central role when comparing two data sets.

An economist might compare the money spent on food with the household income. A criminologist might compare monthly crime rates with average temperature. A political scientist might compare historic voting rates with rainfall figures for each relevant Thursday. A football fan might be interested in whether the number of points obtained before the New Year is an indicator of the number of points a team will achieve over the whole season.

▶ A line of best fit on a scatter diagram and a correlation coefficient are tools to help you make predictions and to quantify the extent to which two variables are related

For example, the correlation between the temperature on a given day in Manchester and Southampton is strong, whereas the correlation between the temperature in Manchester and Sydney, Australia is weak.

> Galton found that the correlation between a parent's and a child's heights is not perfect and some random factors contribute a 'scatter'. As a result, if a parent is of above average height, then the child is less likely to be as much above average. For example, Galton found that the children of parents who were 3 inches above average were typically only 2 inches above average height. He called this phenomena regression to the mean and the whole subject is now often referred to as regression analysis.

Preparation

Before you start this chapter, you should be able to
- **Plot points on a grid having chosen suitable scales**
1 On a grid, plot these points   A (2, 5)   B (−11.7, 4.1)
                                   C (−6, −7)   D (3, −5)
- **Draw a line through two points**
- **On a given straight line, find the value of _x_ [or _y_] given the value of _y_ [or _x_]**
2 Draw a line through the given pair of points and from the line find
   i) _y_ when _x_ = −3   **ii)** _x_ when _y_ = −3
   a) AC   **b)** BD
- **Given an equation of a straight line, find the coordinates of points on it**
3 On the line $7.2x + 2.14y = 37.3$
   a) find the value of _y_ when   **i)** _x_ = 2.9   **ii)** _x_ = −2.9
   b) find the value of _x_ when   **i)** _y_ = −2.43   **ii)** _y_ = 0

Challenge

People are fascinated by the weather and love to try to find patterns in its behaviour and use these to try to predict future weather.

For two cities or towns of your choice investigate the correlation between their temperatures, total hours of sunshine and rainfall in different months.

3.1 Scatter diagrams and correlation

Scatter diagrams

> ▶ A scatter diagram is a way to visualise patterns which may be present in a pair of variables

The maximum temperature in Manchester and Southampton (in °C) was found on the third day of each month in 2011. The data are given below.

Date	Maximum temperature (°C)	
	Manchester, x	Southampton, y
3rd January	2	3
3rd February	9	9
3rd March	7	5
3rd April	12	13
3rd May	15	15
3rd June	24	24
3rd July	23	21
3rd August	25	24
3rd September	19	19
3rd October	24	22
3rd November	16	16
3rd December	10	12

Source: Weather underground!

To display the results on a scatter diagram, first, draw and label two axes, one for each variable. Plot each point using the paired data as the coordinates. For example, for January with temperatures 2 °C in Manchester and 3 °C in Southampton, the point is plotted at (2, 3). The scatter diagram shows the data for the twelve months.

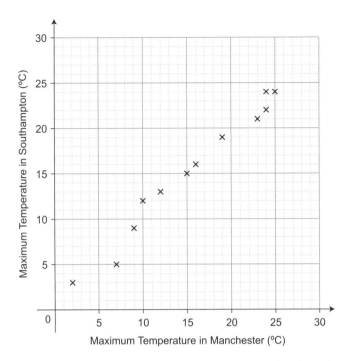

Maximum Temperature in Manchester (°C)

As you would expect, the scatter diagram above shows that there is an apparent link between the temperature in Manchester and the temperature in Southampton. Here the data appear to lie close to a straight line.

> ► If a straight line gives a good description of the points on a scatter graph then the variables are said to have a **linear relationship**

It is not necessary for the data to lie on or close to a straight line but when it does it is easier for you to analyse the data.

Correlation

From a scatter diagram, one of three conclusions can be made about the linear relationship between the two variables.

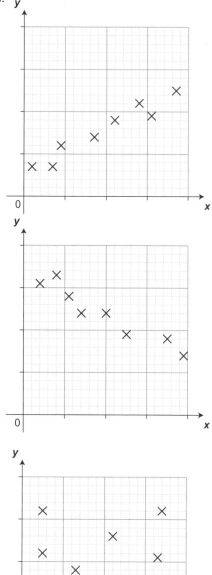

1 The scatter diagram shows that the two variables have a positive correlation.

> ▶ For a **positive correlation**, as x increases y increases

If the points are close to a straight line the correlation is called a strong positive correlation. If the points are more scattered, the correlation is called a weak positive correlation.

2 The scatter diagram shows that the two variables have a negative correlation.

> ▶ For a **negative correlation**, as x increases y decreases

If the points are close to a straight line, the correlation is called a strong negative correlation. If the points are more scattered, the correlation is called a weak negative correlation.

3 The scatter diagram shows that the two variables have no correlation.

> ▶ For **no correlation**, the points are widely scattered showing that there is no link between the variables

Example 1

The heights and weights of seven students were measured. The results were recorded in pairs for each student. For example, the student with height 172 cm had weight 62.3 kg

Student	A	B	C	D	E	F	G
Height (cm)	172	165	147	152	181	135	185
Weight (kg)	62.3	58.3	55.1	59.1	64.7	68.2	65.2

a) Display the results on a scatter diagram.
b) It is believed that one of the results was recorded incorrectly. Identify which result was likely to have been recorded incorrectly.
c) Excluding the incorrectly recorded data point, state the type of correlation shown by the scatter diagram.

- -

a) The scatter diagram shows the height/weight of the seven students.

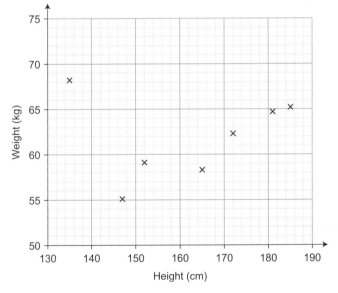

b) The result that was likely to have been recorded incorrectly was for student F as its 'point' is a long way from a line drawn through the other points.
c) Ignoring this incorrect data point, the scatter diagram shows a strong positive correlation.

Line of best fit

If there is a perfect linear correlation between the two variables the points plotted on a scatter diagram will all lie on a straight line. If the two variables have a strong correlation then the points will be close to a straight line, rather than on it.

> ▶ A **line of best fit**, also known as a **regression line**, can be drawn 'by eye' to pass as near to as many of the points as possible

In general, the line will have approximately as many data points above it as below it. It also must pass through a fixed point determined by the values of the first variable, x, and the values of the second variable, y.

p.6

> ▶ A line of best fit must pass through the **mean point** $(\bar{x}, \bar{y})$, where $\bar{x}$ is the mean of the first set of data and $\bar{y}$ is the mean of the second set of data

You can use the line to estimate values for one variable when you are given values for the other variable: either y given x or x given y.

> Section **3.3** on regression lines shows you how to calculate the equation of the line of best fit, when a greater degree of accuracy is required.

Example 2

The Office of National Statistics reported on the number of passengers passing annually through British airports. The data below compares the data for 2001 with the data for 2006.

Airport	Number of passengers (millions)	
	2001	**2006**
Birmingham	7.71	9.05
Heathrow	60.45	67.3
Liverpool	2.25	5.0
Southampton	0.85	1.9
Stansted	13.65	23.7

a) Find the mean point.

▶ Continued on next page

b) Plot a scatter diagram of the data.

c) Draw a line of best fit through the mean point.

d) The number of passengers passing through Gatwick airport in 2006 was 34 million.

Using your scatter diagram, estimate the number of passengers passing through Gatwick airport in 2001.

---

a) (17, 21.4)

b, c)

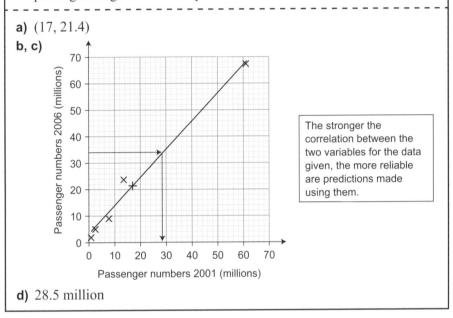

The stronger the correlation between the two variables for the data given, the more reliable are predictions made using them.

d) 28.5 million

When you are asked to predict the value of one variable given the value of the other variable using a line of best fit, there are two cases to consider depending on whether the given variable lies inside the range of the existing data.

The first case is called interpolation and the second case is called extrapolation.

• If yes then the prediction should be reliable.

• If no then the prediction may not be reliable.

In example **2d,** the prediction should be reliable because 34 million is inside the range 0 – 67 million.

If you try to use the line of best fit to predict the number of passengers passing through Atlanta, Georgia in 2001 given that 86 million passengers passed through in 2006, than the prediction will be unreliable for two reasons. First, 86 million is outside the range of the available data. Second, Atlanta is a US airport where different relationship might apply.

Exercise 3.1

1 A block of ice is melting. The weight, in kilograms, which has not yet melted is recorded after certain periods of time. The data found is given in the table.

Time, x (minutes)	10	15	20	25	30
Weight not melted, y (kg)	5.1	4.2	3.5	3.1	2.8

a) Draw the scatter diagram for the data.
b) Calculate $\bar{x}$ and $\bar{y}$.
c) Draw a line of best fit.
d) From your graph, estimate the length of time when the weight of ice, which has not melted, is
   i) 4 kg   ii) 3 kg.

2 An experiment was carried out to measure the height to which a rubber ball bounced after being dropped from various heights.

Height of drop, x (metres)	1.0	1.4	1.5	1.8	2.0
Height of bounce, y (centimetres)	75	90	120	140	150

a) Draw the scatter diagram for the data.
b) Calculate $\bar{x}$ and $\bar{y}$.
c) Draw a line of best fit.
d) From your graph, estimate
   i) the height of the bounce when the ball is dropped 1.9 m
   ii) the height from which the ball is dropped if the ball bounces 1 m.

3 In an experiment, a number of bacterial cultures were grown in a laboratory. After a number of days, the number of bacteria, in millions, was recorded.

Age, x (days)	1	2	3	4	5	6	7
Number of bacteria, y (millions)	5	12	17	24	29	35	42

a) Draw the scatter diagram for the data.
b) Calculate $\bar{x}$ and $\bar{y}$.
c) Draw a line of best fit.
d) From your graph, estimate
   i) the age when the number of bacteria is 20 million
   ii) the age when the number of bacteria is 40 million.

4 The areas and populations of some English counties are given below. The populations are for the year 2003.

County	Area (square miles)	Population (millions)
East Sussex	693	0.74
Hampshire	1458	1.64
Isle of Wight	147	0.13
Kent	1441	1.55
West Sussex	768	0.75

a) Plot a scatter diagram of the data.

b) Draw a line of best fit through the mean point.

c) The area of another county, Buckinghamshire, is 727 square miles. Estimate the population of Buckinghamshire.

5 Eight apple trees were measured and the measurements are given below.

Height, x (metres)	4.45	3.3	3.2	2.9	4.1	3.7	4.6	4.3
Circumference, y (cm)	31	24	25	22	28	26	34	32

a) Draw the scatter diagram for the data.

b) Calculate $\bar{x}$ and $\bar{y}$.

c) Draw a line of best fit.

d) From your graph, estimate

    i) the height of a tree which has a circumference of 30 cm

    ii) the circumference of a tree which has a height of 3.5 m.

6 Tim wants to buy a certain model of car. He finds the price and age of a number of cars that are for sale. The data found are given below.

Age, x (years)	1	4	5	6	10	11	12
Price, y (£)	10 800	5450	4895	4095	475	300	140

a) Draw a scatter diagram for the data.

b) Calculate $\bar{x}$ and $\bar{y}$.

c) Draw a line of best fit.

d) From your graph, estimate

    i) the price of a car which is 3 years old

    ii) Tim can spend £6000. What age of car could Tim buy?

Pearson's product moment correlation coefficient

A **correlation coefficient** is used to quantify how closely two variables are related. Karl Pearson invented one such measure for how close two variables are to having a linear relationship.

▶ Pearson's **product moment correlation coefficient**, r, measures how closely a line of best fit can be drawn to the actual data points

The product moment correlation coefficient takes values between 1 and −1.

▶ In an examination you will be expected to use your calculator to find the product moment correlation coefficient

A value of +1 means that the data points all lie on the line of best fit which has a positive gradient.

A correlation between 0.5 and 1 is regarded as strong. It indicates that if x increases than you expect y to increase.

A value of −1 means that the data points all lie on the line of best fit which has a negative gradient.

A correlation between −0.5 and −1 is also strong. It indicates that if x increases then you expect y to decrease.

▶ The sign of the product moment correlation coefficient is the same as the sign of the gradient of the line of best fit

---

Example 3

p.72

For the data in section **3.1** on the maximum temperatures in Manchester and Southampton

a) Find Pearson's product moment correlation coefficient.

b) Comment on your results.

- -

a) Using a calculator the value of the product moment correlation coefficient is 0.98737

b) This implies that there is a very strong positive correlation between the temperature in Manchester and the temperature in Southampton.

```
LinearReg
 a =0.91835147
 b =1.01555209
 r =0.9873688
 r²=0.97489716
MSe=1.39634525
y=ax+b
                  COPY DRAW
```

Correlation and causality

Often, it is natural to link the changes in two variables. For example, the height of a child is likely to depend on his or her age. You would expect an average six-year-old to be taller than an average five-year-old. The one year difference has allowed the child time to grow, causing an increase in height.

The notion of causality is very important in the real world. For example, you might work for a pharmaceutical company that is introducing a new drug for Alzheimer's disease. To obtain regulatory approval, you must demonstrate that the drug does not cause any serious side effects. Your trials show you that your patients have an above average incidence of hip fractures. Is this a causal effect of your drug or does it just reflect the fact that your patients are older people who are more susceptible to falls?

> Here the age of the patients is an example of a confounding variable.

> ▶ When deciding whether two variables are causally related you must check that any correlation is not the result of a third variable

Even if two variables have a high Pearson's coefficient, then this does not necessarily mean that one variable causes the other to change.

The graph shows the percentage of people who smoke in the UK, x, and the annual number of road deaths in the UK, y, from 1980 to 2010. The percentage of smokers has decreased and the number of road deaths has decreased: a decrease in x has coincided with a decrease in y.

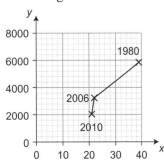

This does not mean that the change in x caused the change in y. It is more plausible to suggest that x decreased because of government health campaigns, an increase in the cost of cigarettes and the smoking ban in pubs and restaurants that occured between 1980 and 2010. Whereas y decreased because of improved car design and road improvements. The changes were almost certainly independent, rather than the result of causality.

> ▶ Causation can result in correlation   but correlation does not imply causation

Non-linear relationships

Sometimes two variables are related but a straight line is not the best curve to fit the data.

The graph shows measurements of the height, h metres, of a ball t seconds after it is thrown in the air.

Initially, when t increases, h increases but then h decreases. There is a relationship between h and t but it is not a straight line.

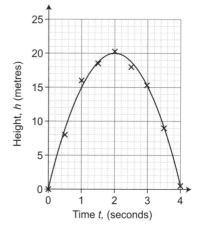

The size of a population is often strongly correlated with the age of the population. Such data is often described by an exponential function: if the population doubles then so does its rate of growth. That is until another factor changes such as the birth rate or the availability of food. The world population over the last millennium shows such an exponential growth.

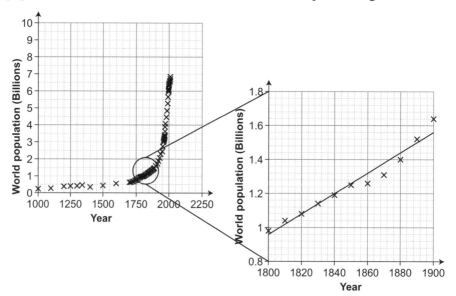

However over a shorter time period, here the nineteenth century, it may be possible to use a linear model.

Exercise 3.2

1 The energy consumed in the UK by various users was recorded over the period from 1970–2010.
The data for some years is given in the table.

Year	Energy used (1000 tonnes of oil equivalent)		
	Industry	Transport	Domestic
1970	62 300	28 200	36 900
1975	55 400	30 900	37 100
1980	48 300	35 500	39 800
1985	41 700	38 500	42 100
1990	38 700	48 600	40 800
1995	36 300	50 200	42 700
2000	35 500	55 500	46 900
2005	32 300	58 800	47 800
2010	27 500	55 700	48 500

Source: Office for National Statistics

Find Pearson's product moment correlation coefficient for
a) the industry and transport data,
b) the industry and domestic data,
c) the transport and domestic data.
d) Hence state which pair of data are more strongly correlated.
e) State the percentage changes in energy used between 1990 and 2010 for each of these categories.

2 For each region in England, the percentage of household waste recycled during 2009/10 and the percentage increase in traffic on major roads between 1999 and 2009 was recorded. The data are shown in the table.

Region	Traffic increase %	Waste recycled %
North East	9.1	34.7
North West	9.2	38.5
Yorkshire and Humber	8.4	36.8
East Midlands	7.3	45.6
West Midlands	7.8	40.0
East	6.8	46.1
London	−6.3	31.8
South East	4.2	40.0
South West	11.6	43.5

Source: Office for National Statistics

a) Find Pearson's product moment correlation coefficient for the two sets of data. *(2 marks)*

b) Hence state whether the two sets of data are likely to be linearly related. *(1 mark)*

c) Ken considers that a region which has a higher recycling rate will also try to reduce the increase in traffic. Does the data support this view? *(3 marks)*

3 Hermione, who is studying reptiles, measures the length, x cm, and the weight, y grams, of a sample of 11 adult snakes of the same type. Her results are shown in the table.

Snake	A	B	C	D	E	F	G	H	I	J	K
x	46	39	54	79	47	58	73	35	43	51	36
y	55	48	58	88	61	55	82	51	50	66	57

a) Calculate the value of the product moment correlation coefficient, r, between x and y. *(3 marks)*

b) Interpret your value in context. *(2 marks)*

c) Draw a scatter diagram for these data. *(2 marks)*

d) Subsequently it is found that, of the 11 adult snakes, 9 are male and 2 are female.

Given that female adult snakes are generally larger than male adult snakes, identify the 2 snakes which are most likely to be female.

(*1 mark*)

(AQA 2009)

4 For each of the following graphs of *y* versus *x*

i) Describe the correlation

ii) Estimate the size of the product moment correlation coefficient: is it negative or positive, strong or weak or zero

iii) State whether any relationship is linear or non-linear

a)

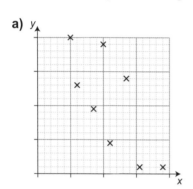

b)

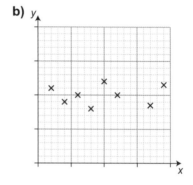

c)

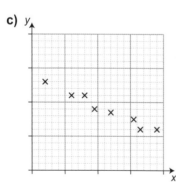

d)

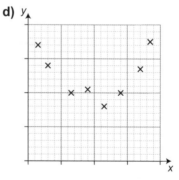

5 Give two examples each of a pair of variables which satisfy the following criteria.

a) Positive correlation and causal connection.

b) Negative correlation and causal connection.

c) Positive correlation and no causal connection.

d) Negative correlation and no causal connection.

3.3 Regression lines

In section **3.1** after drawing a scatter diagram, you added a line of best fit to the diagram to show the general trend of the data points. Since this was done 'by eye' it is subject to your personal judgement: different people may draw different lines.

It is also possible to calculate the equation of a line of best fit, the regression line, and so remove any personal judgement.

> ▶ In an examination you will be expected to use your calculator to find the equation of the regression line

p.76

The line must pass through the mean point, ($\bar{x}$, $\bar{y}$).

The standard method used to find the regression line is known as the 'method of least squares' which gives the equation of the regression line of y on x to be $y = ax + b$

> Check carefully whether your calculator gives $y = ax + b$ or $y = a + bx$ and also check carefully in the question which of these equations is required.

You should be able to interpret the values of a and b.
For the equation $y = ax + b$,

the constant term b is the value of y when x is zero.

the coefficient of x a is the slope or gradient of the line. That is, the increase in the value of y when x increases by 1 unit.

Exam technique
To draw the regression line

1 Find the mean point
2 Use the equation of the regression line to find another point on the line
3 Join these two points with a straight line

> In an examination you are expected to show that you have found this additional point.

Example 4

For the data in section **3.1** on the maximum temperatures in Manchester, x, and Southampton, y

a) Calculate the equation of the regression line of y on x giving your answer in the form $y = ax + b$.

b) Interpret, in context, your values of a and b.

----

a) Using a calculator the equation of the regression line is

$$y = 0.9184x + 1.0156$$

```
LinearReg
  a =0.91835147
  b =1.01555209
  r =0.9873688
  r²=0.97489716
  MSe=1.39634525
y=ax+b
                   COPY DRAW
```

b) The value of b indicates that when the temperature in Manchester is $0\,°C$, the temperature in Southampton is expected to be $1.0156\,°C$.

The value of a indicates that if Manchester is warmer by $1\,°C$, then Southampton is expected to be $0.9184\,°C$ warmer.

Example 5

The table shows the times taken, y minutes, for a wood glue to dry at different air temperatures, $x\,°C$.

x	10	12	15	18	20	22	25	28	30
y	42.9	40.6	38.5	35.4	33.0	30.7	28.0	25.3	22.6

a) Calculate the equation of the least squares regression line $y = a + bx$ *(4 marks)*

b) Estimate the time taken for the glue to dry when the air temperature is $21\,°C$.   *(2 marks)*

                                  (AQA 2008)

----

a) Using a calculator the equation of the regression line is
$$y = 53.06736 - 1.00337x$$

b) $y = 53.1 - 1.00 \times 21 = 32.1$
Estimated time = 32 minutes

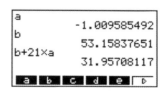

```
a             -1.009585492
b             53.15837651
b+21×a        31.95708117
  a   b   c   d   e   ▷
```

Exercise 3.3

1 A random sample of 10 males is chosen. The heart rates, x beats per minute, and body temperatures, y °F, of these males are shown in the table.

Heart rate, x (beats per min)	70	73	75	68	74	73	78	77	82	78
Body temperature y (°F)	96.3	97.1	97.1	97.4	97.6	97.8	98.0	98.6	98.6	98.8

a) Plot the above data as a scatter graph. *(2 marks)*

b) Use your calculator to find
  i) the mean heart rate, $\bar{x}$, and the mean body temperature, $\bar{y}$
  ii) the correlation coefficient between y and x.
  iii) the equation of the line of best fit in the form $y = ax + b$, giving the values of a and b correct to 3 significant figures. *(5 marks)*

c) Draw the line of best fit on your scatter graph. *(3 marks)*

d) Interpret, in the context of this question, the value of a from the line of best fit. *(2 marks)*

(AQA 2008)

2 Data on the amount of CO_2 produced per person (metric tonnes) and the amount of CO_2 per GDP (in metric tonnes per US \$) was found for a number of countries. The data are given below.

Country	CO_2 produced per person, x (tonnes)	CO_2 per GDP, y (tonnes per \$)
Austria	8	0.90
Belgium	12	1.10
Denmark	11	1.08
Finland	12	1.28
France	6	0.78
Germany	10	1.19
United Kingdom	9	1.17

Source: NationMaster.com

a) Plot the above data as a scatter graph.   (*2 marks*)

b) Use your calculator to find
  i) the mean amount of CO_2 produced per person, $\bar{x}$ (*1 mark*)
  ii) the mean amount of CO_2 per GDP, $\bar{y}$ (*1 mark*)
  iii) the product moment correlation coefficient
    between y and x (*2 marks*)
  iv) the equation of the line of best fit in the form
    $y = ax + b$, giving the values of a and b correct to 3
    significant figures.   (*2 marks*)

c) Draw the line of best fit on your scatter graph.   (*4 marks*)

3 The average ages at which women and men first marry for some countries are given in the table below.

Country	Women, x (years)	Men, y (years)
Austria	27.9	30.3
Finland	28.3	30.5
France	29.1	31.2
Germany	28.2	30.9
Italy	27.1	30.0
Netherlands	28.3	30.7
Norway	28.6	31.1
Spain	29.1	31.2
Sweden	30.4	32.9
United Kingdom	27.7	29.8

Source: NationMaster.com

a) Plot the above data as a scatter graph.   (*2 marks*)

b) Use your calculator to find
  i) the mean age of women, $\bar{x}$
  ii) the mean age of men, $\bar{y}$ (*3 marks*)
  iii) the product moment correlation coefficient
    between y and x (*2 marks*)
  iv) the equation of the line of best fit in the
    form $y = ax + b$, giving the values of a and b correct
    to 3 significant figures.   (*2 marks*)

c) Draw the line of best fit on your scatter graph.   (*4 marks*)

Investigation – Bivariate data

Karl Pearson was a British mathematician who made significant contributions to the early development of statistics, including the correlation coefficient, the concept of hypothesis testing and the chi-squared test. In 1901 he founded *Biometrika*, one of the first academic journals dedicated to statistics and data analysis.

1 Investigate Pearson's contributions to mathematics and science.

Weather

In both 1976 and 2012, extended periods of dry weather in Britain led to the imposition of restrictions on water usage. On both occasions the drought was suddenly followed by a period of extended rainfall.

In 1976, three days after Denis Howell was appointed Minister for Drought, heavy rains caused widespread flooding and he became known as Minister for Floods.

2 Use UK weather statistics to identify periods when prolonged dry spells were followed by extreme wet spells. Do such periods of drought correspond to periods of high temperature?

ICT opportunity

Use a spread sheet or similar program to investigate fitting non-linear curves to data.

Research

You can characterise data sets using their means, standard deviations and correlation coefficient, however these can be deceptive.

3 Find *Anscombe's quartet*: for each data set calculate $\bar{x}$, $\bar{y}$ σ_x, σ_y and the correlation coefficient, then plot the data and add the line of best fit from your calculator.

4 You have seen how to find a line of best fit both 'by eye' and using the 'least squares' method built into your calculator. Investigate other methods of finding a line of best fit such as the median-median line.

Hydroelectric power

Paraguay produces 99.9% of its electricity from hydroelectric power. Portugal produces 31.3% of its electricity from hydroelectric power.

5 Do countries which produce a significant proportion of their electricity by hydroelectric schemes have similar climates?

6 Are there any correlations between a country's climate and other sources of renewable energy such as solar power or biomass. Is it possible to make predictions for how much energy could be generated this way in the U.K.

Project

The following three weather-related topics could provide you with the basis for a project.

- Consider long-term weather statistics for various countries to investigate whether there is evidence of global warming.

- By considering both onshore and offshore wind turbines, investigate the average efficiency of a wind turbine in different regions of the UK and in other countries. Is there a correlation with the prevailing wind, its strength and consistency in different seasons?

- Consider the years in the UK which have had the coldest winters and the most snowfall. Is there any correlation with the weather statistics of the preceding year(s) or the following year(s) which could help in long-range weather forecasts?

Consolidation

You should now be able to
- Draw and interpret a scatter diagram and draw a line of best fit
- Use a calculator to find Pearson's product moment correlation coefficient and interpret its value
- Use a calculator to find the equation of the regression line, $y = ax + b$
  Plot two points on the line and draw the line
- Interpret the coefficients a and b in context

1 The table shows the length, in centimetres, and maximum diameter, in centimetres, of each of 10 honeydew melons selected at random from those on display at a market stall.

Length	24	25	19	28	27	21	35	23	32	26
Maximum diameter	18	14	16	11	13	14	12	16	15	14

   a) Calculate the value of the product moment correlation
      coefficient.   (*3 marks*)
   b) Interpret your value in the context of this question.   (*2 marks*)
                                                                (AQA 2007)

2 Use *Toddlers* on data sheet **3**
   a) Plot this data as a scatter diagram.
   b) Use your calculator to find
      i) the mean length and the mean weight
      ii) the equation of the regression line of w on l.   (*5 marks*)
   c) Plot the regression line of w on l on the scatter diagram. (*4 marks*)
   d) Briefly interpret the gradient of the regression line
      of w on l.   (*2 marks*)
   e) Use the regression line to estimate the weight of an
      unknown boy whose length is 65 cm.   (*2 marks*)
   f) Estimate the age of a boy who weighs 7.5 kg.   (*1 mark*)

3 The table shows, for each of a random sample of eight paperback fiction books, the number of pages, x, and the recommended retail price, £y, to the nearest 10p.

x	223	276	374	433	564	612	704	766
y	6.50	4.00	5.50	8.00	4.50	5.00	8.00	5.50

a) Calculate the value of the product moment correlation coefficient between x and y. *(3 marks)*

b) Interpret your value in the context of this question. *(2 marks)*

c) Suggest one other variable, in addition to the number of pages, which may affect the recommended retail price of a paperback fiction book. *(1 mark)*

(AQA 2006)

4 Use *Climate averages* on data sheet **3**

The Quarter 1 and Quarter 3 differences are repeated in this table.

Year	2001	2002	2003	2004	2005	2006	2007	2008	2009
Quarter 1 (x)	−0.2	1.9	0.5	0.9	0.9	−0.5	2.0	1.3	−0.1
Quarter 3 (y)	0.4	0.3	1.3	0.7	0.7	2.3	−0.3	0.0	0.5

a) Use your calculator to find

   i) the mean for the Quarter 1 differences and the mean for the Quarter 3 differences *(2 marks)*

   ii) the correlation coefficient between x and y *(1 mark)*

   iii) the equation of the regression line of y on x. *(2 marks)*

b) Plot the regression line of y on x on a scatter graph. *(4 marks)*

c) Use your regression line to predict the Quarter 3 difference given that the Quarter 1 difference in 2010 is −0.9 *(2 marks)*

d) The correlation coefficient between Quarter 2 and Quarter 3 is 0.054. Which Quarter, 1 or 2, is the better one to use in order to predict Quarter 3? Justify your answer. *(1 mark)*

(AQA 2011)

4 Normal distributions

Over time data have been collected on a great many measurements and the distributions of their values investigated. For example

- Heights and weights
- The fraction of heads that occur when a fair coin is tossed many times
- The number of emails a busy person receives each working day
- The size of the errors made when measuring the positions of planets
- The speeds of molecules in a gas

Despite their variety, the distributions of these measurements all look remarkably similar when drawn on a suitable x-axis. Since the same simple distribution arises in so many fields it is not surprising that it has acquired several names. Statisticians and mathematicians call it the 'normal distribution' physicists usually call it the 'Gaussian distribution' and social scientists call it the 'bell curve'.

▶ The normal distribution is an excellent approximation to many other distributions found in the real world
It provides a simple, 'universal' distribution whose shape can be fully described by giving the values of its mean, μ, and standard deviation, σ

The normal distribution describes a continuous distribution but it can also be used successfully to approximate discrete distributions. This is especially true if lots of small factors contribute to the final results. For example, all the individual coin tosses contribute to the fraction of heads occurring. The normal distribution is probably the most important and widely used theoretical model in statistics.

Preparation

Before starting this chapter, you should be able to

- **Round to two decimal places or three significant figures**
1 Round to   **i)** 2 decimal places   **ii)** 3 significant figures
   a) 321.481   **b)** 0.0026741

- **Find the mean and standard deviation**
2 Find the   **i)** mean   **ii)** standard deviation
   of the data sets   **a)** 17, 13, 32, 25, 38, 38, 22, 16, 30, 29, 15, 42
                 b) 0.56, 0.19, 0.88, 0.04, 0.45, 0.33, 0.30, 0.72

- **Find a percentage of a number**
3 Find 17% of 2840

- **Calculate basic probabilities**
4 A random number has a probability of 0.75 of being less than 2 and a probability of 0.4 of being less than 1. What is the probability that the number is
   a) greater than 2   **b)** greater than 1   **c)** between 1 and 2

Challenge

When you buy a packet of biscuits you may notice that the packet usually states a weight, say, 200 grams e. It is impossible that an individual packet will weigh almost exactly 200 grams; some will be overweight and the rest will be underweight.

Find the accurate weights of the contents of a number of packets of groceries and compare this to the weight on the label.

When would it be reasonable to complain that a packet is being mis-sold and is underweight? If you bought five packets all of which were underweight would that be grounds for complaint?

4.1 The normal distribution

The idea of a person's IQ, or intelligence quotient, was developed by Lewis Terman in 1916. The distribution of IQ scores of the general population in the UK forms a normal distribution with mean 100 and standard deviation 15. If you found the IQ score for each person in a village of 1000 people and plotted a histogram of the IQ scores you would expect to obtain a graph similar to the one shown below.

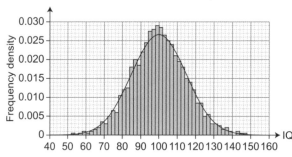

> Whilst intelligence is continuous, IQs are quoted to the nearest integer.

> 40 people have an IQ in the range 86 to 88. The relative frequency is 40 ÷ 1000 = 0.04. The frequency density is 0.04 ÷ (88 − 86) = 0.02

The graph uses relative frequences, that is frequences divided by the total number of data points so that the area under the curve is one. This helps to make the shape of the graph independent of the actual population of the village. It also means that an area under the curve gives the probability of someone from the village having an IQ in that range.

The histogram is symmetrical with the mean and median coinciding with the mode, which gives the most common IQ score as 100.

> For a symmetric distribution the mean and median must be equal.

The distribution has a typical 'bell shaped' curve: the probability of obtaining a particular IQ score falls rapidly the further it is from the mean.

> Strictly you can only give a probability for a range of values. The probability of a particular value is zero for a continuous distribution.

As the IQ data illustrates, in real life it is rare to see a perfect version of this curve. However as more people are included in the histogram, say from a city rather than a village, then the more closely it should match the ideal shape.

p.48

The vertical axis on the histogram is the 'frequency density' which reminds you that it is the area under a part of the curve which gives the probability of obtaining a result in that range of IQs. Since the IQ score of every person is shown on the histogram, the area under the complete curve is 1.

The main features of the normal distribution are

▶ The distribution is bell shaped
▶ The distribution is symmetrical: mean = median = mode
▶ The total area under the curve is 1

For a normal distribution, about $\frac{2}{3}$ of the data is within one standard deviation of the mean, about 95% of the data is within two standard deviations of the mean and 99.7% is within three standard deviations of the mean.

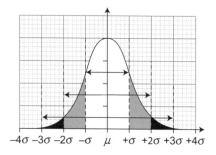

For the IQ data:

$\frac{2}{3}$ of the data is between 85 and 115
95%   of the data is between 70 and 130
99.7% of the data is between 55 and 145

$P(\mu-\sigma<x<\mu+\sigma)$	$=68\%$
$P(\mu-2\sigma<x<\mu+2\sigma)$	$=95\%$
$P(\mu-3\sigma<x<\mu+3\sigma)$	$=99.7\%$

The shape of the normal distribution is completely determined by the values of its mean, μ, and standard deviation, σ.

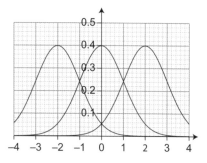

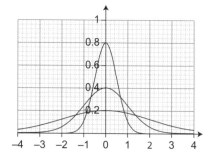

$\sigma = 1$; from left to right $\mu = -2, 0, +2$
As μ increases the distribution moves to the right.

$\mu = 0$; from top to bottom $\sigma = 0.5, 1, 2$
As σ increases the distribution becomes wider and lower; the area remains equal to unity.

▶ The mean fixes the position of the centre of the distribution

▶ The standard deviation fixes the width and height of the distribution

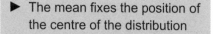

Given a bell-shaped distribution, special techniques are available to find the mean and standard deviation of a suitable normal distribution with which to model the data. You can estimate approximate values as follows.

- The mean is the position of the line of symmetry of the distribution.
- The standard deviation is either half of the symmetric range that contains two-thirds of the data or one-sixth of the range that contains all of the data.

For example, the graph shows the weights of packets of biscuits which are to be described by a normal distribution.

mean $\approx$ 202 grams
standard deviation
$\approx (204 - 200) \div 2 = 2$ grams
or $\approx (210 - 194) \div 6 = 2.7$ grams

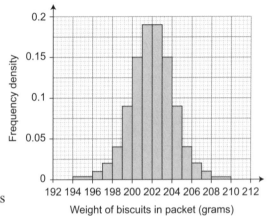

Exercise 4.1

1 Match the six graphs with the six pairs of values of the mean, μ, and standard deviation, σ.

a) $(\mu = 0, \sigma = 2)$ **b)** $(\mu = 3, \quad \sigma = 0.5)$ **c)** $(\mu = -0.5, \sigma = 1)$
d) $(\mu = 2, \sigma = 1)$ **e)** $(\mu = -3, \sigma = 0.75)$ **f)** $(\mu = -3, \quad \sigma = 0.5)$

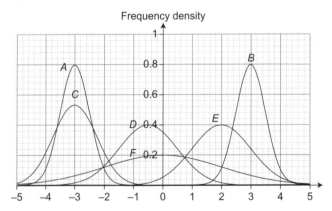

2 In each of the parts below sketch a normal distribution with the given mean, μ, and standard deviation, σ.

a) μ = 10, σ = 6   **b)** μ = 30, σ = 2

c) μ = 5, σ = 0.1   **d)** μ = 100, σ = 8

3 State whether the distributions shown below appear to form a normal distribution. If the distribution is not normal give the reason.

a)

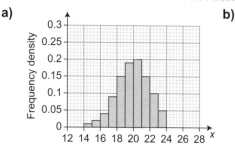

b)

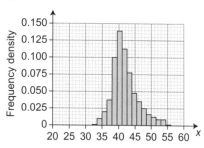

4 Estimate the mean and standard deviation of each of the normal distributions sketched below.

a)

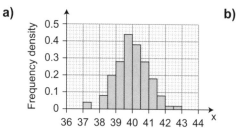

b)

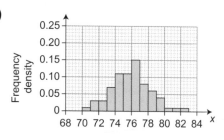

c)

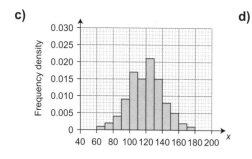

d)

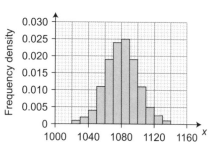

5 Using the methods of sections **2.2** and **2.3** estimate the means and standard deviations of the four data sets in question **4**. How do they compare to the values you obtained in question **4**?

> Use the frequency density in place of frequency.

Standardised scores and finding probabilities

> ▶ A standard normal distribution has mean 0 and standard deviation 1

p.103

This might not appear to be a very typical distribution to study but, using transformations, all normal distributions can be related to this one standard normal distribution.

> See the Algebra book, section 2.5

As you saw in exercise **4.1**, the normal distributions appear to have different shapes but the area under the complete curve is always 1 and the same proportion is always the same number of standard deviations from the mean.

> ▶ By convention, z is used to denote a standard normal variable
> ▶ The function $\Phi(z)$ is the probability that a random value from the standard normal distribution is less than or equal to the given value, z
> $$\Phi(z) = P(x \le z)$$

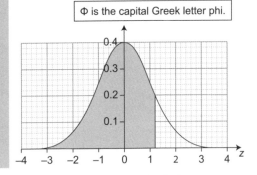

Φ is the capital Greek letter phi.

Thus $\Phi(1.2)$ is the probability that z is less than 1.2 and is the shaded area shown in the sketch.

The areas under the curve are difficult to calculate, fortunately there are tables which give you the values. A set of tables is provided at the end of this book. Your calculator should also able to give you these values.

> ▶ A table of the standard normal distribution will be supplied to you in the examination

The table gives the probability that a normally distributed variable, with mean = 0 and standard deviation = 1, is less than or equal to z.

To use normal distribution tables

1. Round the value of z to two decimal places
2. Find the row starting with the first two digits
3. Move along the row to the column containing the second decimal place.

> Rather than truncate z it is possible to use interpolation but this is not necessary in A-level Use of Mathematics.

For example, to find $\Phi(1.84)$ find the row in the table starting with 1.8 (the first two digits) and move along to the column containing the 0.04

z	0.00	0.01	0.02	0.03	0.04	0.05	0.06	0.07	0.08	0.09
1.8	0.9641	0.9649	0.9656	0.9664	0.9671	0.9678	0.9686	0.9693	0.9700	0.9706

From the table, you find $P(x \le 1.84) = \Phi(1.84) = 0.9671$

You can also use a calculator to find probabilities for a standard normal distribution.

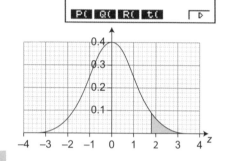

If you wish to find the probability of a value of z being more than 1.84, which is the area shown shaded, you use the fact that the total area under the curve is 1. Thus the area required is $1 - \Phi(1.84) = 1 - 0.9671$ or 0.0329

► $P(x > z) = 1 - P(x \le z) = 1 - \Phi(z)$

It is always useful to draw a sketch showing which region you are finding. This can be used to decide which z values to evaluate.

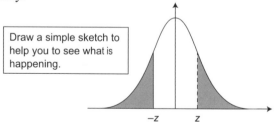

Standard normal tables are usually only supplied for positive z values equivalent to cumulative probabilities greater than a half. To find Φ for negative arguments use symmetry.

► $\Phi(-z) = 1 - \Phi(z)$

Draw a simple sketch to help you to see what is happening.

For example,
$\Phi(-0.6745) = 1 - \Phi(0.6745)$
$= 1 - 0.75$
$= 0.25$

Example 1

Find the probability that z lies between 0.97 and 1.84, that is
$P(0.97 < z < 1.84)$

This area is shown shaded on the graph.
The area to the left of 1.84
is $\Phi(1.84) = 0.9671$
The area to the left of 0.97
is $\Phi(0.97) = 0.8340$
The area required is
$0.9671 - 0.8340 = 0.1331$

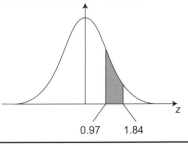

To find the probability of z lying between two values, you can use both symmetry and the fact that the total area is 1.

Example 2

Find the probability that z lies between -2.03 and -1.42, that is, $P(-2.03 < z < -1.42)$

> Negative values of z are to the left of the mean.

This area is shown shaded on the graph.
This area is the same area as between $+2.03$ and $+1.42$
As in example **1**, this is
$\Phi(2.03) - \Phi(1.42)$
$= 0.9788 - 0.9222$
$= 0.0566$

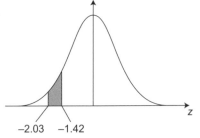

Example 3

Find the probability that z lies between -0.74 and $+0.81$, that is, $P(-0.74 < z < 0.81)$

This area is shown shaded on the graph.
By symmetry, the area to the left of -0.74 is the same as the area to the right of 0.74 which is equal to
$1 - \Phi(0.74) = 1 - 0.7704 = 0.2296$
The area to the left of 0.81 is
$\Phi(0.81) = 0.7910$
Probability is $0.7910 - 0.2296 = 0.5614$

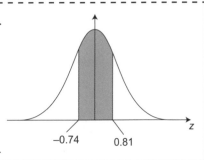

The manufacturer of the packets of biscuits discussed in section **4.1** states that the packets have a mean weight of 200 grams and a standard deviation of 2.5 grams.

A randomly selected packet of biscuits weighs 204 grams. What is the probability that a packet, chosen at random, weighs at least 204 grams?

Tables of the normal distribution with mean 200 and standard deviation 2.5 do not exist. However you can overcome this problem if you use standardised values of the mean and standard deviation. The crucial value is the number of standard deviations which the value under consideration is away from the mean.

The packet is $204 - 200 = 4$ grams from the mean or $4 \div 2.5 = 1.6$ standard deviations from the mean. You can now use tables to find $P(z \geq 1.6) = 1 - 0.9452 = 0.0548$ That is, there is just over a one in twenty chance of picking a packet that weighs at least 204 grams.

The value 1.6 is known as the **standardised value** z or z score.

▶ For a value of x, taken from a normal distribution with mean μ and standard deviation σ, the standardized value z is given by

$$z = \frac{x - \mu}{\sigma} \quad \text{or} \quad z = \frac{\text{value} - \text{mean}}{\text{standard deviation}}$$

Example 4

The lengths of leaves from a particular plant may be assumed to be normally distributed with mean 17.3 cm and a standard deviation of 3.2 cm.

Find the standardised values of   **a)** 19.2 cm   **b)** 28.3 cm

- -

Using the formula given above

a) The z value of 19. 2 cm $= \dfrac{19.2 - 17.3}{3.2} = \dfrac{1.9}{3.2} = 0.594$

b) The z value of 28.3 cm $= \dfrac{28.3 - 17.3}{3.2} = \dfrac{11}{3.2} = 3.44$

Exercise 4.2

1 Use the tables for the normal distribution – or use your calculator – to find the probability that a measurement from a standard normal distribution will be less than
   a) 2.01   **b)** 1.14   **c)** 1.07   **d)** 0.08

2 Use the standard normal table to find the following
   a) $P(z < 1.75)$ **b)** $P(z < 1.41)$ **c)** $P(z < 0.81)$ **d)** $P(z < 3.14)$

3 Use the tables for the normal distribution – or use your calculator – to find the probability that a measurement from a standard normal distribution will be more than
   a) 1.19   **b)** 1.29   **c)** 2.84   **d)** 0.67

4 Use the standard normal table to find the following
   a) $P(z > 1.85)$ **b)** $P(1 < z < 1.52)$
   c) $P(0.1 < z < 1.29)$ **d)** $P(2 < z < 3)$

5 Use the tables for the normal distribution – or use your calculator – to find the probability that a measurement from a standard normal distribution will be between
   a) −1.7 and 1.31   **b)** −0.61 and 0.88
   c) −1.1 and 1.18   **d)** −1.7 and −1.01
   e) −1.91 and −1.07   **f)** −2.5 and 0.5

6 The lengths of a particular species of fish may be assumed to be normally distributed with mean 19.3 cm and a standard deviation of 4.8 cm.
   Find the standardised values of
   a) 23.4 cm   **b)** 17.6 cm   **c)** 19.3 cm   **d)** 4.8 cm

7 The time which train travellers spend queuing to buy a ticket may be assumed to be normally distributed with mean 5.2 minutes and a standard deviation of 2.2 minutes. Find the standardised values of
   a) 6.3 minutes   **b)** 3.8 minutes   **c)** 0 minutes   **d)** $\frac{1}{4}$ hour

8 Packs of minced beef on sale in one supermarket may be assumed to be normally distributed with mean 275 grams and a standard deviation of 8 grams. Find the standardised values of

a) 284 grams b) 255 grams c) 290 grams d) $\frac{1}{4}$ kilogram

9 The weights of loaves of a particular type of bread may be assumed to be normally distributed with mean 810 grams and a standard deviation of 10 grams. Find the standardised values of

a) 800 grams b) 825 grams c) 816 grams d) 0.806 kg

10 The weight of pebbles on a beach may be assumed to be normally distributed with mean 120 grams and a standard deviation of 30 grams. Find the standardised values of

a) 185 grams b) 72 grams c) 96 grams d) 0.163 kg

11 When Zoe phones for a taxi, she knows that the time before the taxi arrives at her house is normally distributed with mean 14 minutes and a standard deviation of 4 minutes. Find the time she should phone for the taxi if she wants

a) a probability of 0.95 that the taxi will arrive by 7:00 pm

b) a probability of 0.99 that the taxi will arrive by 7:00 pm

c) a probability of 0.995 that the taxi will arrive by 7:00 pm

d) a probability of 0.1 that the taxi will arrive after 7:00 pm

> To solve P(z) = 0.95 you can use the standard tables in 'reverse' or your calculator.
>
> ```
> Inverse Normal
>     x=1.64485363
> ```

12 A company supplies wooden shelves in two sizes. The measurements of both sizes of shelf are normally distributed. What is the interquartile range for the lengths of each size of shelf if

a) Large shelves: mean = 1120 mm, standard deviation = 2.5 mm

b) Small shelves: mean = 640 mm, standard deviation = 1.7 mm

Applications of normal distributions

In real life the manufacturer of the packets of biscuits discussed in section **4.1** will do their best to ensure all the packets have a very similar weight. The manufacturer will be trying to make the standard deviation as small as possible. However, on average, half the packets will be below average and half will be above average. The contents of a packet marked average weight 200 grams will half the time be less than the contents of any packet marked minimum weight 200 grams. To 'be safe' manufactures often set the production mean higher than the nominal weight on the packet.

The techniques of section **4.2** are used regularly in the real world to find the probability of many events occurring.

Example 5

The weights of the contents of jars of jam are normally distributed with a mean of 284 grams and a standard deviation of 2.1 grams.

Find the probability that the contents of a jar will weigh

a) more than 286 grams

b) less than 280 grams

---

a) For 286 grams:

$$z = \frac{286 - 284}{2.1} = \frac{2}{2.1} = 0.952$$

$$\begin{aligned} P(x > 286) &= 1 - P(x \le 286) \\ &= 1 - \Phi(0.952) \\ &= 1 - 0.8289 \\ &= 0.1711 \end{aligned}$$

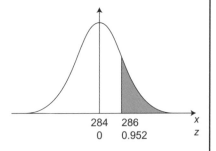

b) For 280 grams:

$$z = \frac{280 - 284}{2.1} = \frac{-4}{2.1} = -1.905$$

By symmetry $\Phi(-1.905) = 1 - \Phi(1.905)$

$$\begin{aligned} P(x < 280) &= 1 - \Phi(1.905) \\ &= 1 - 0.9713 \\ &= 0.0287 \end{aligned}$$

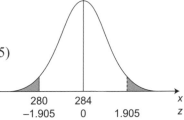

Example 6

The contents of jars of jam are normally distributed. The manufacturer of the jam knows that the machines have a standard deviation of 2.1 grams and requires no more than 1% of the jars to have contents under 280 grams. Find the mean weight of the jam which the manufacturer should use.

- -

It is required that 1% are under 280 grams. This means that the probability of being over 280 grams is 0.99

$P(x < 280) = 1\% \Leftrightarrow P(x \geq 280) = 99\%$

Using the tables $0.99 = \Phi(2.33)$

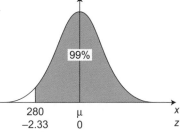

In a standard normal distribution 99% of the values are below 2.33
That is, 1% of the values are above 2.33
By symmetry, this gives 1% of the values are below −2.33

$$z = \frac{\text{value} - \text{mean}}{\text{standard deviation}}$$

$$-2.33 = \frac{280 - \text{mean}}{2.1}$$

$-2.33 \times 2.1 = 280 - \text{mean}$

$\text{mean} = 280 + 2.33 \times 2.1 = 284.89 = 284.9$ grams

Example 7

The weights of packets of biscuits have a normal distribution with mean 200 grams and standard deviation 2.5 grams. According to legislation the tolerable error on a 200 gram packet is 4.5%. To be allowed to use the e symbol, the probability that a packet is more than this error underweight must be less than 6% and below twice this error must be zero. What are these two probabilities for the weight of a packet of biscuits?

- -

4.5% of 200 = 9

$P(x < 200 - 9) = \Phi\left(\frac{-9}{2.5}\right) = \Phi(-3.6) = 0.000159 \qquad < 6\%$

$P(x < 200 - 2 \times 9) = \Phi\left(\frac{-18}{2.5}\right) = \Phi(-7.2) = 3 \times 10^{-13} \quad \text{effectively zero}$

Exercise 4.3

1 Body temperatures may be assumed to be normally distributed with a mean of 98.3 °F and a standard deviation of 0.8 °F.
Calculate the probability that a person, chosen at random, has a body temperature greater than 100.5 °F

2 The wrist circumference for boys may be assumed to be normally distributed with a mean of 155 mm and a standard deviation of 11.2 mm.
Calculate the probability that a boy, chosen at random, has a wrist measurement
a) greater than 162 mm   **b)** less than 158 mm
c) less than 146 mm   **d)** between 145 and 165 mm

3 The heights of boys aged 11 years may be assumed to be normally distributed with a mean of 149.3 cm and a standard deviation of 12.7 cm.
Calculate the probability that a boy, chosen at random, has a height
a) greater than 152 cm   **b)** less than 154 cm
c) less than 145 cm   **d)** between 148 and 151 cm

4 Each day, Margot completes the crossword in her local morning newspaper. Her completion times, X minutes, can be modelled by a normal random variable with a mean of 65 and a standard deviation of 20.
Determine
a) $P(X < 90)$ **b)** $P(X > 60)$ *(5 marks)*
(AQA 2010)

5 Electra is employed by E and G Ltd to install electricity meters in new houses on an estate. Her time, X minutes, to install a meter may be assumed to be normally distributed with a mean of 48 and a standard deviation of 20.
Determine
a) $P(X < 60)$ *(2 marks)*
b) $(30 < X < 60)$ *(3 marks)*
c) the time, k minutes, such that $P(X < k) = 0.9$ *(4 marks)*
(AQA 2007)

6 Assume that the wrist circumference of the male population of the UK is normally distributed with a mean of 184.5 mm and a standard deviation 13.6 mm.

    a) A manufacturer designs a watch for the UK market. It is designed to cater for wrist circumferences up to 205 mm.
What percentage of the UK male population is catered for by these watches? *(4 marks)*

    b) A watch designed for the Japanese market will fit wrists with circumferences from 145 mm to 190 mm.
Find the percentage of the UK male population that this watch will fit. *(6 marks)*

                                                                          (AQA 2005)

7 The rest pulse rate of a randomly-selected person can be assumed to be normally distributed with mean 68 and standard deviation 13. Find the probability that:

    a) i) a person has a pulse rate over 75

       ii) a person has a pulse rate between 58 and 72

    b) Find the pulse rate below which 90% of the population lie.

8 A set of ear plugs claims to have noise reduction of 25 dB, if used properly. At low frequency (125 Hz), the plugs are found to have a mean attenuation of 31.6 dB with standard deviation 4.3 dB. Assume the attenuations are normally distributed. What is the probability that a set of plugs chosen at random will have attenuation below the advertised 25 dB?

9 An engineering firm receives an order to supply 10 000 nails. The firm's machines produce nails with lengths having mean 55 mm and standard deviation 1.5 mm. Quality control rejects a nail if it is less that 52 mm long or more than 57 mm long. To be sure of making enough good nails to fulfil the order the firm decides to produce 11 000 nails. Assuming a normal distribution for the lengths of nails, how many nails which will not be rejected is the firm likely to produce?

Investigation – normal distributions

Several mathematicians were involved in the development of the normal distribution including Abraham de Moivre, Pierre-Simon Laplace and Carl Friedrich Gauss.

Research

Find about their contributions to understanding the normal distribution and to other parts of mathematics and science.

Everyone believes in the normal law, the experimenters because they imagine that it is a mathematical theorem and the mathematicians because they think it is an experimental fact.

Gabriel Lippmann (1845 – 1921)

One reason for the ubiquity of the normal distribution is the central limit theorem.

1 What does this theorem say?
2 Find situations where people use the normal distribution to describe real data.

ICT opportunity

Investigate the distribution of the sum of $n = 1, 2, 4, 8$ or 16 random numbers: $x_n = R_{\#1} + R_{\#2} + \ldots + R_{\#n}$.

Also investigate the distribution of the scaled numbers

$$y_n = \frac{x_n - \frac{n}{2}}{\sqrt{\frac{n}{12}}}$$

Normal distributions are used by derivatives traders in financial markets. Did a lack of understanding of the mathematics behind complex financial products designed to maximise profit and minimise risk contribute to the financial crash of 2007?

You trade a commodity – a raw material such as coffee, oil or pork bellies or perhaps a portfolio of mortgage loans – and want to arrange a future purchase or sale at an agreed price. For example, you could represent an airline trying to fix the price of

The idea is not new. The Dojima Rice Exchange in Osaka, Japan, founded in 1710, was the first modern futures exchange.

aircraft fuel now for the year ahead. Such a futures contract is an example of a derivative.

Crucial to understanding the risks involved in buying or selling a commodity now for delivery in the future is your ability to assess future prices, say as measured by an annual percentage price change. You could use historical data to estimate an average annual rate. However you also know, that in the short term, prices will fluctuate up and down about the mean annual rate. This gives you a daily value for the equivalent annual rate and the standard deviation of these rates is a measure of the market volatility. One model for future price changes is a normal distribution with mean the historic annual rate, μ, and standard deviation the historic volatility, σ.

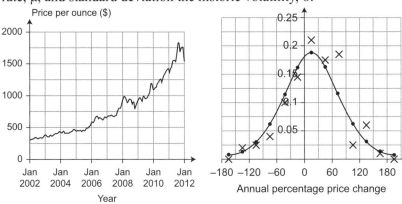

The graph on the left shows the historic price of gold at the end of every month between 2002 and 2011. The graph on the right shows the distribution of annualised percentage price rises that occurred each month over this period. Also shown is a normal distribution given by a mean historic price change $\mu = +20\%$ and a historic volatility $\sigma = 65\%$.

Using this model the probability of a price rise next year $= \Phi(-20/65) = 0.352$

3   Calculate the probabilities of price changes in the ranges
   a) 0 to 20%   **b)** 20 to 40%   **c)** −20 to 0%   **d)** −40 to −20%

Project

Find historical data on the annual percentage price changes for three commodities over the last ten years.
Using your data, calculate the mean annual rates and the historic volatilities for each commodity. Use your results and the normal distribution model to predict the probabilities of future price changes.

Consolidation

1 A biologist is investigating the size of mature fish caught in a river. The length of the fish follows a normal distribution with a mean of 17.5 cm and a standard deviation of 2.5 cm. The fish are classified as large, medium and small according to their length. Fish that are longer than 21.5 cm are classified as large.
   a) Calculate the probability that a fish is classified as large.

   (3 marks)

   The probability that a fish is classified as small is 0.127
   b) Calculate the maximum length of a fish that would be classified as small. *(4 marks)*

2 a) Assume that Japanese adult males have foot lengths which are normally distributed with a mean of 24.9 cm and standard deviation 1.05 cm.
      Calculate the probability that a Japanese adult male has a foot length greater than 27 cm. *(4 marks)*
   b) Assume that Japanese adult females have foot lengths which are normally distributed with a mean of 22.8 cm and standard deviation 0.89 cm.
      Calculate the percentage of the Japanese adult female population that has foot lengths between 22 cm and 25 cm. *(5 marks)*

   (AQA 2011)

3 a) The heights of UK men may be considered to have a normal distribution with a mean 178 cm and standard deviation 7 cm. The height of a standard doorway is 190 cm. Calculate the percentage of UK men that are too tall to pass through a standard doorway without bending. *(4 marks)*

b) The height of US women may be considered to have a normal distribution with a mean 162 cm and standard deviation 6.4 cm. The United States army requires that women's heights be between 147 cm and 203 cm. Calculate the percentage of US women that satisfy this requirement.

(5 marks)

(AQA 2010)

4 The heights of sunflowers may be assumed to be normally distributed with a mean of 185 cm and a standard deviation of 10 cm. Determine the probability that the height of a randomly chosen sunflower

a) is less than 200 cm *(3 marks)*

b) is more than 175 cm *(3 marks)*

c) is between 175 cm and 200 cm. *(2 marks)*

(AQA 2006)

5 When a particular make of tennis ball is dropped from a vertical distance of 250 cm on to concrete, the height, X centimetres, to which it first bounces may be assumed to be normally distributed with a mean of 140 and a standard deviation of 2.5

a) Determine

i) $P(X < 145)$ *(3 marks)*

ii) $P(138 < X < 142)$ *(4 marks)*

b) Determine, to one decimal place, the maximum height exceeded by 85% of first bounces. *(4 marks)*

(AQA 2008)

Data sheet 2

Ashes series

In summer 2009, Australia and England played a series of five test matches in the Ashes series. In each match, 11 players from each team can bat for each of their two innings. This gives a possible total of 22 innings per team per match.

The data below shows the runs scored by each player from the England team. For several reasons, including bad weather, only 95 innings were made by England players, out of a possible total of 110.

The table shows the number of runs scored in these 95 innings.

Number of runs scored	Number of innings
0 – 5	25
6 – 10	10
11 – 20	13
21 – 30	15
31 – 50	13
51 – 70	12
71 – 80	4
81 – 100	1
101 – 150	1
151 – 200	1
201 – 255	0

(AQA 2011)

Heights of men

The heights of 150 men were found. The data are given below.

Height, h (cm)	Number of men
$0 < h \le 110$	1
$110 < h \le 150$	4
$150 < h \le 160$	14
$160 < h \le 170$	29
$170 < h \le 180$	38
$180 < h \le 190$	35
$190 < h \le 200$	21
$200 < h \le 220$	7
$220 < h \le 240$	1

Number of passengers on a plane

The numbers of passengers on 120 planes arriving at an airport on one day were recorded.

The data are shown below.

Number of passengers, p	Number of planes
$0 < p \le 40$	1
$40 < p \le 60$	4
$60 < p \le 100$	11
$100 < p \le 120$	22
$120 < p \le 130$	38
$130 < p \le 150$	42
$150 < p \le 180$	2
Over 180	0

Supermarket

A supermarket recorded the amount spent, in pounds, by each of the 150 customers who passed through one checkout on one morning. The data are given in the table below.

Amount spent, a (£)	Number of customers
$0.00 < a \leq 10.00$	3
$10.00 < a \leq 20.00$	12
$20.00 < a \leq 30.00$	10
$30.00 < a \leq 35.00$	15
$35.00 < a \leq 40.00$	24
$40.00 < a \leq 50.00$	29
$50.00 < a \leq 60.00$	18
$60.00 < a \leq 80.00$	22
$80.00 < a \leq 90.00$	10
$90.00 < a \leq 100.00$	5
$100.00 < a \leq 110.00$	2
Over 110.00	0

(AQA 2008)

Triathlon

The London triathlon was held on the weekend of the 4th and 5th August 2007. The Olympic standard triathlon consists of a 1500 metre swim, a 40 kilometre cycle and a 10 kilometre run.

The athletes were divided into groups with a staggered start over the two days so that there was minimal congestion.

The data below relates to one group who competed on the 5th August. Of these athletes, 336 completed the course in under 4 hours. The times taken by these 336 athletes are given in the table.

Time taken, t (minutes)	Number of athletes
$0 < t \leq 120$	0
$120 < t \leq 130$	4
$130 < t \leq 140$	19
$140 < t \leq 150$	77
$150 < t \leq 160$	83
$160 < t \leq 170$	70
$170 < t \leq 180$	36
$180 < t \leq 190$	33
$190 < t \leq 200$	9
$200 < t \leq 210$	1
$210 < t \leq 220$	4
Over 220	0

(AQA 2009)

Data sheet 3

Toddlers

Young children grow at different rates.
Lengths and weights shown are average
for boys in a given month after birth.

Age	Length, l (cm)	Weight, w (kg)
birth	49.9	3.35
1 month	54.7	4.47
2 months	58.4	5.57
3 months	61.4	6.38
4 months	63.9	7.00
5 months	65.9	7.51
6 months	67.6	7.93
7 months	69.2	8.30
8 months	70.6	8.62
9 months	72.0	8.90
10 months	73.3	9.16
11 months	74.5	9.41
12 months	75.7	9.65
13 months	76.9	9.87
14 months	78.0	10.09
15 months	79.1	10.31

Source: World Health Organisation

Climate averages

The World Meteorological Organisation (WMO) requires the calculation of averages for consecutive periods of thirty years. However, many WMO members, including the UK, update their averages at the completion of each decade. Thirty years was chosen as a period long enough to eliminate year-to-year variations. These averages help to describe the climate and are used as a base with which current conditions can be compared.

For 2001–2009, the table below gives differences between the temperature for each quarter and the corresponding average for that quarter during 1971–2000.

The temperatures (°C) are for the South of England.

Year	Quarter 1	Quarter 2	Quarter 3	Quarter 4
2001	−0.2	0.5	0.4	0.7
2002	1.9	0.7	0.3	0.9
2003	0.5	1.5	1.3	0.2
2004	0.9	1.3	0.7	0.5
2005	0.9	1.0	0.7	0.6
2006	−0.5	1.3	2.3	1.9
2007	2.0	1.9	−0.3	0.4
2008	1.3	1.0	0.0	0.5
2009	−0.1	1.4	0.5	0.5

(AQA 2011)

Practice paper 1 – data sheet

Populations

The populations of a number of countries and the percentages of those populations who are under 15 years old and between 15 and 64 years old were recorded as in the table below.

	Percentage aged under 15	Percentage aged between 15 and 64	Total population
Belgium	16.9	65.7	10 379 067
France	18.4	65.2	60 876 136
Germany	14.4	66.7	82 422 299
Portugal	16.6	66.3	10 605 870
UK	17.7	66.5	60 609 153

Source: NationMaster.com

Number of books read

Keen readers often join book clubs. Some of these are national institutions, set up to enable readers to access books more economically.
There are also local book clubs, some of which are based on libraries.
Members meet to discuss and evaluate the books which they have read.

Crossword

The time taken to 'solve' a crossword can, for easy crosswords, be only a few minutes. It is common for the cryptic crosswords published in the 'serious newspapers' to take a few hours.

Human body

The lengths, in cm, of the forearm plus hand and of the forearm were recorded in a survey of 25 men. Their heights were also recorded. The data are given below.

Forearm plus hand (cm)	Forearm (cm)	Height (cm)
47.2	27.6	191
46.8	26.1	183
42.1	24.9	168
44.7	26.1	173
42.7	24.8	177
39.8	23.9	159
46.8	26.8	191
48.2	28.9	197
41.2	24.6	165
39.8	24.1	158
45.2	27.1	167
43.7	25.1	179
48.1	28.5	198
41.4	24.8	164
42.5	24.9	170
43.6	25.3	169
44.1	25.2	173
46.2	26.9	188
39.9	24.2	161
40.3	24.4	163
41.2	24.7	166
42.3	25.2	169
46.4	25.9	186
41.6	24.9	168
41.7	24.6	167

Practice paper 1 – questions

SECTION A
Use *Populations* on the Data Sheet

1 a) Calculate the percentage of people in France who are
over 64 years old. *(1 mark)*
b) Calculate the number of people in Portugal who are
under 15 years old. *(2 marks)*
c) In Qatar there are 209 830 people aged 15 or under.
This is 23.7% of the population of Qatar.
Calculate the population of Qatar. *(3 marks)*

SECTION B
Use *Number of books read* on the Data Sheet

2 The number of books that 100 women had read in the last year
was found.
The data are shown in the table.

Number of books, n	$0 \le n \le 10$	$11 \le n \le 20$	$21 \le n \le 30$	$31 \le n \le 40$	$41 \le n \le 100$
Number of women	28	38	21	7	6

For these women, calculate estimates of
a) the mean *(2 marks)*
b) the standard deviation. *(3 marks)*

SECTION C
Use *Human body* on the Data Sheet

3 a) Draw a scatter diagram to represent the data for the length of the
forearm plus hand and the length of the forearm for the 25 people
measured in the survey. *(2 marks)*
b) i) Use your calculator to find the correlation coefficient
between the length of the forearm plus hand and the length
of the forearm for the 25 people measuredin the survey. *(2 marks)*
ii) Comment on this correlation coefficient. *(2 marks)*

c) i) Calculate the equation of the regression line of the length of the forearm plus hand on the length of the forearm in the form $y = ax + b$, giving the values of a and b correct to two decimal places. *(2 marks)*

ii) Write down two pairs of coordinates on the regression line. Hence draw the regression line on the scatter diagram. *(4 marks)*

iii) Interpret the value of a in context. *(2 marks)*

iv) Use the equation of the regression line to predict the length of the forearm plus hand for a person with a forearm measurement of 28 cm. *(2 marks)*

4 a) The back-to-back stem and leaf diagram given below shows the heights of 25 women.

Height (cm)

Women		Men
	19	
	18	
4 3 2 2 1	17	
7 5 5 4 4 4 2	16	
9 8 8 6 4 3 3 2	15	
7 5 3 2 1	14	

Key | 15 | 8   means 158 cm

On a copy of this back-to-back stem and leaf diagram, add the data from the Data Sheet showing the heights of the 25 men. *(2 marks)*

b) Find
  i) the median height of those surveyed
  ii) the interquartile range of those surveyed. *(3 marks)*

c) Compare the heights of the women and the men. *(2 marks)*

SECTION D
Use *Crossword* on the Data Sheet

5 The time taken to complete a crossword may be assumed to be normally distributed with a mean of 152 minutes and a standard deviation of 30 minutes.
Calculate the probability that a person, chosen at random, takes
a) more than 182 minutes *(3 marks)*
b) between 142 and 200 minutes. *(3 marks)*

Practice paper 2 – data sheet

Birth announcements

Carl Roberts always reads the columns of announcements in his local weekly newspaper.

During each week of 2011, he notes the number of births announced. His results are summarised in the table.

Number of births	1	2	3	4	5	6	7	8
Number of weeks	4	1	6	15	5	18	2	1

Darts

The section of a dartboard is divided into many regions.

The score achieved when a dart hits the board is between 1 and 60.

Baggage

Passengers on a 'full service' airline flying within Europe usually have a baggage allowance of one piece of checked luggage which has a maximum weight of 23 kg. Frequent flyers and business passengers usually have an allowance of two checked bags, both up to 23 kg.

The weights of luggage, w (kg), belonging to each of the 146 passengers on one plane were recorded and the data are as shown below.

Weight, w (kg)	$10 \leq w < 16$	$16 \leq w < 20$	$20 \leq w < 23$	$23 \leq w < 35$	$35 \leq w < 45$	$45 \leq w$
Number of passengers	21	36	81	2	6	0

Heights

When people go to a doctor for their annual check-up the nurse, or doctor, routinely measures and records their weights, in kg, and their heights, in cm. The weights and heights of the population may be assumed to be normally distributed.

Weather

Olivia and Jack are considering going to either South-West France or to Spain for their holiday and find the weather records for the two towns, Bordeaux and Malaga. The records found show, for 2011, the mean daily hours of sunshine per month, the average monthly temperatures and the number of days per month with precipitation.

Mean number of hours of sunshine per month												
Month	Jan	Feb	Mar	Apr	May	Jun	Jul	Aug	Sep	Oct	Nov	Dec
Bordeaux	3.7	3.8	5.6	9.3	9.8	7.0	6.5	7.9	7.3	6.2	4.0	2.6
Malaga	4.8	8.4	6.5	7.0	8.5	10.6	11.8	10.8	9.3	8.2	6.0	7.1

Average monthly temperatures												
Month	Jan	Feb	Mar	Apr	May	Jun	Jul	Aug	Sep	Oct	Nov	Dec
Bordeaux	6.1	8.7	11.1	16.4	18.8	19.3	19.9	21.9	20.2	15.6	13.1	9.7
Malaga	13.3	13.6	14.7	18.1	20.1	23.5	26.8	27.9	24.8	20.8	16.0	14.0

Number of days per month with precipitation												
Month	Jan	Feb	Mar	Apr	May	Jun	Jul	Aug	Sep	Oct	Nov	Dec
Bordeaux	10	17	11	9	7	5	18	13	11	10	15	23
Malaga	9	3	9	6	7	1	0	1	1	4	7	1

Source: WeatherOnline Limited

Practice paper 2 – questions

SECTION A
Use *Birth announcements* on the Data Sheet

1 Carl Roberts always reads the columns of announcements in his local weekly newspaper.

During each week of 2011, he notes the number of births announced. His results are summarised in the table.

Number of births	1	2	3	4	5	6	7	8
Number of weeks	4	1	6	15	5	18	2	1

  a) Calculate the mean, median and mode of these data. *(5 marks)*

  b) State, with a reason, which of the three measures of average in part **a)** you consider to be the most appropriate for summarising the number of births. *(2 marks)*

SECTION B
Use *Darts* on the Data Sheet

2 **a)** Sam regularly practises playing darts and he records the score each dart achieves. For the 50 darts he threw on one day, the scores he achieved are as given below.

Score, s	$1 \leq s < 20$	$21 \leq s < 30$	$31 \leq s < 40$	$41 \leq s < 50$	$51 \leq s < 60$
Frequency	2	6	9	17	16

    i) Draw a cumulative frequency curve to show the data *(3 marks)*

    ii) Find Sam's median score *(1 mark)*

    iii) Find the interquartile range of Sam's scores. *(2 marks)*

  b) John also practises regularly. When he checks his scores, he finds that he has a mean of 41 and an interquartile range of 7. Make two comments that compare the scores achieved by the two players. *(3 marks)*

Use *Baggage* on the Data Sheet

3 The data relating to the weights of luggage belonging to each of the 146 passengers are repeated below.

Weight, w(kg)	$10 \leq w < 16$	$16 \leq w < 20$	$20 \leq w < 23$	$23 \leq w < 35$	$35 \leq w < 45$	$45 \leq w$
Number of passengers	21	36	81	2	6	0

    a) Illustrate the data by means of a histogram.   *(3 marks)*

    b) Calculate an estimate of the mean weight of luggage
        per passenger.   *(2 marks)*

    c) Calculate an estimate of the standard deviation of the
        weights of luggage per passenger.   *(3 marks)*

SECTION D
Use *Heights* on the Data Sheet

4 The heights of men may be assumed to be normally distributed with a mean of 174.3 cm and a standard deviation of 14.8 cm.

Calculate the probability that a man, chosen at random, has a height

    a) greater than 182 mm   *(3 marks)*

    b) between 166 and 180 cm.   *(3 marks)*

5 The data below for Malaga, shows for 2011, the mean daily hours of sunshine per month and the average monthly temperatures.

Month	Jan	Feb	Mar	Apr	May	Jun	Jul	Aug	Sep	Oct	Nov	Dec
Average monthly temperatures, x	13.3	13.6	14.7	18.1	20.1	23.5	26.8	27.9	24.8	20.8	16.0	14.0
Mean number of hours of sunshine per month, y	4.8	8.4	6.5	7.0	8.5	10.6	11.8	10.8	9.3	8.2	6.0	7.1

Source: WeatherOnline Ltd

a) Use your calculator to find for Malaga
- **i)** the mean temperature, $\bar{x}$, and the mean of the daily hours of sunshine per month, $\bar{y}$ *(2 marks)*
- **ii)** the correlation coefficient between y and x *(2 marks)*
- **iii)** the equation of the line of best fit in the form $y = ax + b$, giving the values of a and b correct to 3 significant figures. *(2 marks)*

b) Draw the line of best fit on a copy of the scatter graph. *(2 marks)*

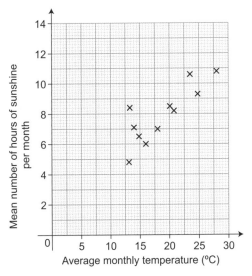

c) Interpret, in the context of this question, the value of a from the line of best fit. *(2 marks)*

Answers

Except for money, all answers are normally given to 3 significant figures

Chapter 1

Preparation

1 **a)** 10 327.56

b) 2.457767473…
= 2.46 (3 s.f.)

2

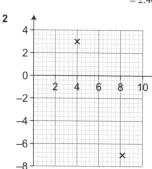

3 **a)** 3.57   **b)** 21.5

Exercise 1.1

1 **a)** $354 \div 20 = 17.7$

b) $(15 + 16) \div 2 = 15.5$

c) 11

2 $549 \div 10 = 54.9$

3 **a)** $275 \div 80 = 3.44$

b) 4

c) 4

4 **a) i)** £ $106.02 \div 70 = £15.15$

ii) No mode   **iii)** £9.10

b) Median

5 $743 \div 31 = 24.0$

6 Mean = $76 \div 50 = 1.52$ Mode = 1,
Median (25th) = 1

7 $1288 \div 200 = 6.44$

8 Total in 5 days is $23.2 \times 5 = 116$ meals
Total in 6 days is $116 + 48 = 164$ meals
Mean is $164 \div 6 = 27.3$

9 Total in 6 tours is $6 \times 32 = 192$
Total in 7 tours is $7 \times 35 = 245$
Number on seventh tour is $245 - 192 = 53$

Exercise 1.2

1 **a)** $36 - 1 = 35$ **b)** 11

c) $(23 + 25) \div 2 = 24$ **d)** $24 - 11 = 13$

2 **a)** $98 - 12 = 86$ **b)** $(29 + 36) \div 2 = 32.5$

c) $(72 + 75) \div 2 = 73.5$

d) $73.5 - 32.5 = 41$

3 **a)** $6 - 1 = 5$ **b)** $5 - 2 = 3$

4 **a)** $56 - 4 = 52$ **b)** $(16 + 14) \div 2 = 15$

c) $(31 + 32) \div 2 = 31.5$

d) $31.5 - 15 = 16.5$

5 **a)** $9 - 3 = 6$ **b)** $6 - 5 = 1$

6 **a)** $72 - 15 = 57$ **b)** $54.5 - 17.5 = 37$

7 **a)** $8 - 0 = 8$ **b)** $4.5 - 1 = 3.5$

8 **a)** $48 - 3 = 45$ **b)** $32 - 9.5 = 22.5$

c) 9.20 am

d) People do not arrive at a waterpark just before lunch.

Exercise 1.3

1 **a)** 70   **b)** 65   **c)** 74

d) 80   **e)** 56

2 **a)** Max = 71, Min = 44
LQ = $(55 + 56) \div 2 = 55.5$
UQ = $(64 + 65) \div 2 = 65$
Median = $(61 + 62) \div 2 = 61.5$

b) The median at 10 pm is much higher, 74 against 61.5: cars travel much slower at 8 am on a weekday morning
The IQRs are similar at both times, 9.5 against 8. The speeds at 10 pm had the greatest range so the majority of cars were travelling in a similar speed range but a few cars were travelling much faster.

3 **a)** Min = 49   Max = 78
LQ = 58   UQ = 70.5
Median = 63.5

b) Min = 39   Max = 82
LQ = 46   UQ = 54.5   Median = 50

c) The new median is much smaller: athletes, times have improved in the training programme.
The IQRs are similar (new 8.5 ~ old 12.5). The new range is much greater (new 43 > old 29); this is because of the one outlier at 82 minutes.

4 a) Min = 5   Max = 249

LQ = 21   UQ = 81.5

Median = 37.5

b) Min = 10   Max = 300

LQ = 151.5   UQ = 232

Median = 192

c) Rachel's friends seem to be more popular than people on average (median 192 > 37.5).

Rachel's friend's show more variation in their numbers of friends (range: 290 > 244, IQR: 80.5 > 60.5).

Most of Rachel's friends only estimated their number of friends so the results may be less reliable.

5 a) Bournemouth: Median = 4.45

Min = 1.5   Max = 7.2

LQ = 1.75   UQ = 5.45

Faro: Median = 8.7

Min = 5.4   Max = 12.6

LQ = 7.4   UQ = 10.85

b) Faro consistently has more hours of sun than Bournemouth (median: 4.45 < 8.7).

The upper quartile for Bournemouth is similar to Faro's lower quartile.

The variation in the hours of sunshine are comparable (range: 5.7 ~ 7.2, IQR: 3.7 ~ 3.45).

Exercise 1.4

1 a) (179 + 182) ÷ 2 = 180.5 cm

b) 117 cm

2 a)

Tuesday		Saturday
9 8 8 7	0	
9 8 7 7 6 5 3 1	10	7 8 9 9
1 1	20	1 5 6 7 8 9
	30	1 2 5 8

Key   0 | 20 | 1

Means   20   Tuesday

and   21   Saturday

b) More passengers fly on a Saturday (median: 15.5 < 20.65).

There is a greater spread in the number of passengers on Saturday (range: 14 < 31, IQR: 9 < 12).

3 a)

February		August
	0	6 9
	10	4 7 9 9
	20	5 7 9 9
	30	4
5 5 2	40	1 2 3 4
8 4	50	
9 8 4 1	60	
3 2 2 2 0	70	
0	80	

Key   0 | 2 | 1

Means   20   February

and   21   August

b) The holidaymakers are younger in August (median: 69 > 27).

The distribution of ages is skewed to older ages in February and younger ages in August.

The overall spreads in ages are similar (range: 42 ~ 38) but there is less variation in ages in February for the central half (IQR: 14 < 24).

4 a) i)

Under 25s		Over 25s
	0	
9 7 5	1	
8 8 6 3 2 0 0	2	1 6
5 5 4 1	3	4 8 9
6	4	2 7 8
	5	1
	6	4 5

Key   0 | 2 | 1

Means   20   Under 25s

and   21   Over 25s

ii) The average number of sessions for under 25s is much lower (IQR: 26 < 42).

The number of sessions for under 25s is more consistent than the number of sessions for the over 25s (range: 31 < 44, IQR: 14 < 17).

Exercise 1.5

1 **a)** $144 \div 10 = 14.4$

  b) 8.32

2 **a)** The mean number of days is +9, this means that the Oak first leafed on average around the 29th April each year.

  b) mean = −12.3

  standard deviation = 6.42

  c) On average, the Oak is first leafing about April 8th in the 90s which is three weeks before it was first leafing in the 50s. The SD is less in the 90s compared to the 50s and thus the numbers are more consistent in the 90s than in the 50s.

  d) These data seem to support the idea of global warming in that the Oak first leaves are much earlier because of the warmer weather.

  OR The claim appears to be correct but it may not be correct, it could just be natural variation.

  OR There is not enough evidence.

3 **a)** **i)** 9

   ii) 2.03

  b) More seeds germinated in the group that were spaced.

  The standard deviation is a little higher for the group that was spaced so these data vary more.

Investigation 1

2 **a)** The greater the range the greater the difference in the number of games won by the top and bottom teams.

  b, e) An increasing IQR/SD suggests an increasing gap between top and bottom teams.

  c) The mean is only sensitive to the number of draws.

  d) A lower median suggests that an 'average' team is losing more often to a top team.

3 The reduction in the number of teams means 41 less games are played each season

Consolidation questions 1

1 **a)** **i)** West Yorkshire
   $836\,148 \div 854\,040 = 0.980$

   ii) North Yorkshire
   $296\,989 \div 237\,583 = 1.25$

  b) Car (and van) ownership per household is greater in the rural area.

2 **a)** Mean = 12.97 or 13.0
   Standard deviation = 0.16

  b) The price of Tbury shares was lower. The prices of Tbury shares varied more than QShop shares.

3 **a)** Min = 42   Max = 173
   LQ = 62.5   UQ = 128
   Median = 97.5

  b) On average there is more rain per month in 2006 (Median: 83 < 97.5)
   The rainfall per month in 2006 is much more spread out than in 2005
   (Range: 83 < 131, IQR: 32.5 < 65.5)

Chapter 2
Preparation

1 **a)** **i)** 4 or 7
   ii) $(4 + 5) \div 2 = 4.5$
   iii) $41 \div 8 = 5.125$
   iv) $11 - 1 = 10$
   v) $(7 + 7) \div 2 - (2 + 4) \div 2 = 4$
   vi) 2.976

  b) **i)** 125
   ii) 125
   iii) $1360 \div 11 = 123.6$
   iv) $145 - 98 = 47$
   v) $133 - 111 = 22$
   vi) 13.30

  c) **i)** none
   ii) 0.57
   iii) $4.37 \div 9 = 0.486$
   iv) $0.78 - 0.08 = 0.70$
   v) $(0.67 + 0.77) \div 2$
      $- (0.19 + 0.23) \div 2 = 0.51$
   vi) 0.247

2 $132 \times 1.07 = 141.2$ cm

3 $8.1 \div 0.215 = 37.7$ kW

Exercise 2.1

1 a) $411 \div 2943 \times 100 = 14.0\%$
  b) $7893 \times 100 \div 25.2 = 31\ 300$
  c) $733 \div 5285 \times 100 = 13.9\%$

2 a) i) $12 \times 46 + 14 \times 36 = 552 + 504 = £10.56$
  ii) $12 \times 60 + 14 \times 50 = £14.20$
  b) $3.64 \div 10.56 \times 100 = 34.5\%$
  c) $46 \times 100 \div 112.2 = 41\text{p}$

3 a) rounding errors
  b) $24.58 \div 100 \times 142\ 732 = 35\ 084$ or $35\ 100$
  c) $2990 \times 100 \div 11.62 = 25\ 732$ or $25\ 700$
  d) No; other areas could be smaller

Exercise 2.2

1 a) $0 - 5$ **b)** $667.5 \div 95 = 28.1$

2 a) $170 - 180$ **b)** $26450 \div 150 = 176$ cm

3 a) $130 - 150$ **b)** $14540 \div 120 = 121$

4 a) $40 - 50$ **b)** $7202.5 \div 150 = £48.02$

5 a) $1600 - 1800$
  b) $146800 \div 100 = £1468$ or $£1470$

6 a) $150 - 160$ **b)** $53870 \div 336 = 160$

7 a) $1 - 5$ **b)** $454 \div 33 = 13.76$ or 13.8

Exercise 2.3

1 a) $125 \div 100 = 1.25$ **b)** 1.12

2 a) 11.1 **b)** 8.90

3 a) 152 **b)** 64.6

4 a) 176 **b)** 19.0

5 a) 121 **b)** 24.3

6 a) 160 **b)** 16.5

7 a) i) 158.235 cm $= 158.24$ cm (2dp)
  ii) $9.0365 = 9.04$ cm (3 sf)
  b) Use of mid-interval values rather than individual values.
  c) i) On average height increases with age for both girls and boys.
     Girls on average taller at 11 and 12 years, but boys are taller at 13 years.
  ii) Standard deviation for boys increases with age implies heights of older boys are more widely spread.

Exercise 2.4

1 a) Class 0–5 freq.den = $25 \div 6 = 4.17$
     Class 6–10 freq.den = $10 \div 5 = 2$
     Class 11–20 freq.den = $13 \div 10 = 1.3$ etc.

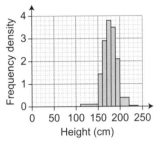

b) i) 29
  ii) $5 + \frac{1}{2} \times 14 = 12$

2 a) Class 0–5 freq.den = $25 \div 6 = 4.17$
     Class 6–10 freq.den = $10 \div 5 = 2$
     Class 11–20 freq.den = $13 \div 10 = 1.3$ etc.

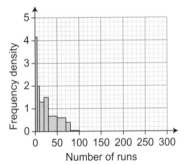

b) i) $25 + 10 + 13 + 15 = 63$
  ii) $4 + 1 + 1 + 1 + \frac{3}{4} \times 12 = 16$
  iii) $\frac{1}{2} \times 4 + 12 + 13 + 15 + 13 + 10 + 25 = 90$

3 a)

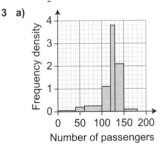

b) i) $11 + 22 + 38 + 42 + 2 = 115$
  ii) $38 + 42 + 2 + \frac{1}{2} \times 22 = 93$

4 a)

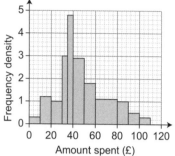

Amount spent (£)

b) i) $18 + 22 + 10 + 5 + 2 = 57$

ii) $22 + 18 + 29 + 24 + 15 + 10 + 12 + 3$
$+ \frac{1}{2} \times 10 = 138$

5 a)

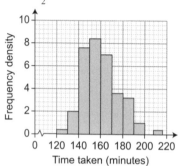

Time taken (minutes)

b) i) $33 + 9 + 1 + 4 = 47$

ii) Number $= 4 + 19 + 77 + 83 + \frac{1}{2} \times 70$
$= 218$

Percentage $= \frac{218}{336} \times 100 = 64.9\%$

6 a)

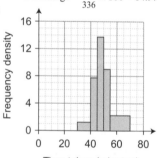

Time taken (minutes)

b) i) $45 + 36 = 81$ **ii)** $\frac{2}{3} \times 36 = 24$

7 a)

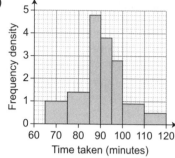

Time taken (minutes)

b) $\frac{3}{5} \times 14 + 9 + 5 = 22$

Exercise 2.5

1 a)

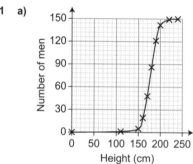

Height (cm)

b) i) 175 cm   **ii)** 165 cm

iii) 185 cm   **iv)** 20 cm

c)

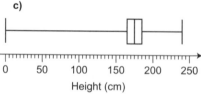

Height (cm)

2 a)

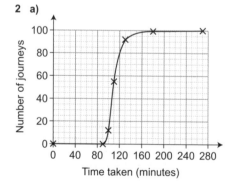

Time taken (minutes)

b) i) 108 min   **ii)** 104 min
iii) 118 min   **iv)** 14 min

c)

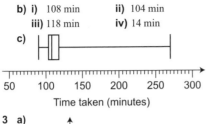

Time taken (minutes)

3 a)

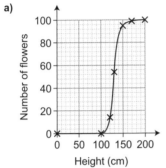

Height (cm)

b) i) 129 cm   **ii)** 124 cm
iii) 139 cm   **iv)** 15 cm

c)

Height (cm)

4 a)

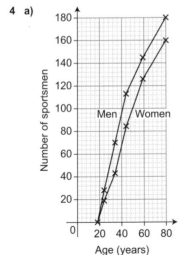

Age (years)

b) Female 43, Male 39
c) On average males and females who suffer 'over exertion' injuries do so at the same age.

5 a)

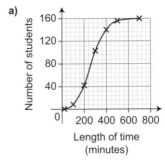

Length of time (minutes)

b) i) 260   **ii)** 190
iii) 340   **iv)** 150

c)

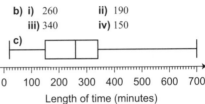

Length of time (minutes)

Exercise 2.6

1 a)

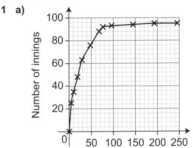

Number of runs scored

b) i) 20   **ii)** 5
iii) 43   **iv)** 43 − 5 = 38
c) 52 runs   **d)** 90th person; 95 percentile

2 a)

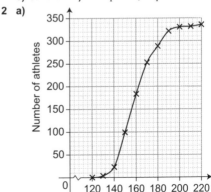

Time taken (minutes)

b) i) 157 min   **ii)** 148 min
iii) 169 min   **iv)** 21 min
c) 134th person, 154 minutes
d) 258th person, 77th percentile

3 a)

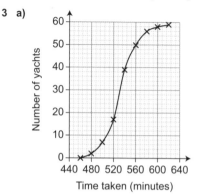

Number of planes vs Number of passengers

b) i) 126   **ii)** 113   **iii)** 137   **iv)** 24
c) 139

4 a)

Number of customers vs Amount spent (£)

b) i) £44   **ii)** £38
iii) £61   **iv)** £23
c) 122th person, 81th percentile

Exercise 2.7

1 a) Rounding errors
b)

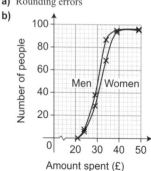

Number of people vs Amount spent (£); Men, Women

c) Female 32, Male 31; age of males is less
2 a) i) £35 125   **ii)** £38 250
b) i) £15 900   **ii)** £13 700
c) On average the women's salaries were lower; the women's salaries were more spread out and nine women had salaries in the highest wage band.

3 a)

Number of yachts vs Time taken (minutes)

b) i) 30th yacht, 532 minutes
ii) 519 minutes
iii) 555 minutes
iv) 36 minutes
c) Min = 460   Max = 620
LQ, median and UQ as above.
d) Median for Sunsail group is larger: they took longer.
The range for Sunsail group is smaller: they are closer together.

4 a)

Number of females vs Income

b) Median = £9880
IQR = £18 200 − £5410 = £12 790
c) Females' incomes in London are (on average) higher than those in the North: medians are £9880 and £7800.
Comparing the interquartile ranges, the females' incomes in the North are less varied than those in London.

5 a)

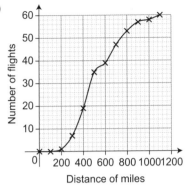

Distance of miles

b) i) 460   **ii)** 370   **iii)** 680   **iv)** 310

c) Min = 100   Max = 1100
LQ, median and UQ as above.

d) On average flights out of Gatwick are longer than those out of Stansted (median 850 > 460). The variation in the length of flights out of Gatwick is larger than for those out of Stansted (range 4310 > 1000, IQR 3100 > 319)

Consolidation questions 2

1 a) Germany

b) $\frac{61\,185\,981 - 60\,816\,701}{60\,816\,701} \times 100 = 0.607\%$

c) $\frac{38\,125\,479 - 38\,115\,641}{38\,125\,479} \times 100 = 0.0258\%$
or −0.0258%

d) 10 045 000 is 99.79%
Population = $\frac{10\,045\,000}{0.9979}$
= 10 066 138 or 10 066 139

2 a) Mean is 41.0 inches   **b)** 4.37 inches

3 a)

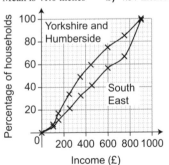

Income (£)

b) Median income is Yorkshire and Humber £365 (±10) South East is £540 (±10)
Median household income for the South East is much higher than that of Yorkshire and Humber.

c) For the SE LQ = £280 (±10);
UQ = £785 (±10) IQR = £505 (±20)
The spread of the household incomes in the South East is greater than that of Yorkshire and Humber.

Chapter 3
Preparation
1

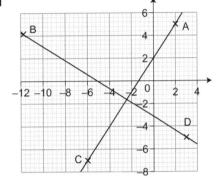

2 a) i) −2.5
   ii) −3.33

b) i) −1.29
   ii) −0.23

3 a) i) 7.67
   ii) 27.19

b) i) 5.90
   ii) 5.18

Exercise 3.1

1 a), c)

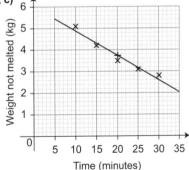

Time (minutes)

b) $\bar{x} = 100 \div 5 = 20$ $\bar{y} = 18.7 \div 5 = 3.74$

d) i) 17.75
   ii) 26.5

2 a), c)

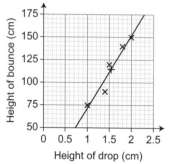

b) $\bar{x} = 7.7 \div 5 = 1.54$ $\bar{y} = 575 \div 5 = 115$

d) i) 144 cm   **ii)** 1.35

3 a), c)

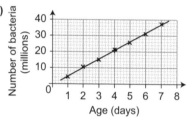

b) $\bar{x} = 28 \div 7 = 4$ $\bar{y} = 164 \div 7 = 23.43$

d) i) 3.43   **ii)** 6.75

4 a), c)

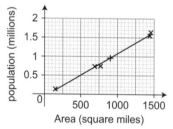

c) 739 000

5 a), c)

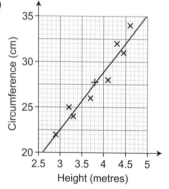

b) $\bar{x} = 30.85 \div 8 = 3.82$ $\bar{y} = 220 \div 8 = 27.75$

d) i) 4.17 m   **ii)** 25.7 cm

6 a), c)

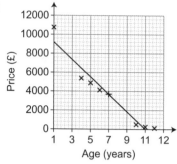

b) $\bar{x} = 49 \div 7 = 7$ $\bar{y} = 26\,155 \div 7 =$ £3736.43

d) i) £7405   **ii)** 4.53 years old

Exercise 3.2

1 a) −0.9448   **b)** −0.92045   **c)** 0.9286

d) The industry and the transport data although they are negatively correlated.

e) Industry −28.9% transport 14.6% domestic 18.9%

2 a) 0.5229

b) The data show a fairly strong positive correlation.

c) No. The data suggests that regions with higher recycling rates have larger increases intraffic.

3 a) 0.8932

b) There appears to be a strong positive correlation between the weight and length of the snakes.

c)

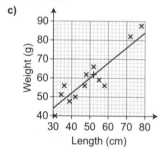

d) Snakes D and G.

4 a) i) Weak negative   **ii)** −0.5
   iii) Linear

b) i) No correlation   **ii)** 0
   iii) Not applicable

c) i) Strong negative   **ii)** −0.9
   iii) Linear

d) i) Strong correlation

   ii) 0, but not applicable

   iii) Non-linear

5 Possible examples are:

  a) Ice cream sales & temperature.

    Shoe size and age.

  b) Fitness level & time for 100 m sprint.

    Value of a car & age of a car.

  c) Ice cream sales & cases of sunburn.

    Intelligence and shoe size.

  d) National literacy level & infant mortality.

    Sales of umbrellas and sales of ice cream.

Exercise 3.3

1 a), c)

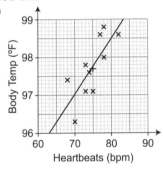

b) i) $\bar{x} = 748 \div 10 = 74.8$

     $\bar{y} = 977.3 \div 10 = 97.7$

  ii) $r = 0.76$

  iii) $a = 0.147, b = 86.7$

  c) Straight line passing through their mean point and through one other calculated point on the correct equation of the line of best fit:

    $y = 0.147x + 86.7$

  d) $a = 0.147$ means that for every 1 beat per minute increase of heart rate the body temperature will increase by $0.147\,°F$

2 a), c)

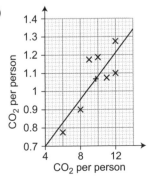

b) i) $\bar{x} = 68 \div 7 = 9.714$

  ii) $\bar{y} = 7.50 \div 10 = 1.07$

  iii) $r = 0.8168$ **iv)** $y = 0.0643x + 0.447$

3 a), c)

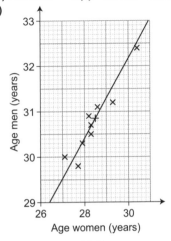

b) i) $\bar{x} = 284.7 \div 10 = 28.47$

  ii) $\bar{y} = 308.6 \div 10 = 30.86$

  iii) $r = 0.9541$ **iv)** $y = 0.910x + 4.96$

  c) Need to use mean point plus one other calculated point to draw line.

Consolidation questions 3

1 a) −0.525 or −0.526

  b) Weak correlation between length and diameter

2 a), c)

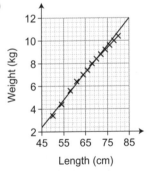

b) i) Mean length $= \bar{l} = 1091.1 \div 16 = 68.2\,\text{cm}$

    Mean weight $= \bar{w} = 126.52 \div 16 = 7.91\,\text{kg}$

  ii) $w = 0.2393l - 8.4109$

  d) The gradient gives the expected increase in weight for each extra centimetre that a boy grows.

  e) $7.14\,\text{kg}$ **f)** 5 months

3 a) r = 0.143

b) Weak or no correlation between number of pages and price.

c) Size, author, publicity, popularity, etc.

4 a) i) $\bar{x} = 6.7 \div 9 = 0.744$

$\bar{y} = 5.9 \div 9 = 0.656$

ii) −0.69

iii) $y = -0.585x + 1.091$

b)

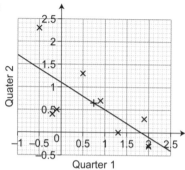

Quarter 1

c) 1.6175

d) It is better to use Q1 because *r* is larger.

Chapter 4

Preparation

1 a) i) 321.48   **ii)** 321

b) i) 0.00   **ii)** 0.00267

2 a) i) 317 ÷ 12 = 26.4   **ii)** 9.53

b) i) 3.47 ÷ 8 = 0.434   **ii)** 0.260

3 0.17 × 2840 = 482.8

4 a) 1 − 0.75 = 0.25   **b)** 1 − 0.4 = 0.6

c) 0.75 − 0.4 = 0.35

Exercise 4.1

1 a – F   b – B   c – E

d – C   e – D   f – A

2 a) Wide graph, centred on 10 and contained within (−8, 28)

b) Narrow graph centred on 30 and contained within (24, 36)

c) Very narrow graph, centred on 5 and contained within (4.7, 5.3)

d) Wide graph, centred on 100 and contained within in (76, 124)

3 a) No, distribution stops at 24.

b) No, not symmetrical

4 a) μ = 40,   σ = 1   **b)** μ = 76,   σ = 2

c) μ = 120,   σ = 20   **d)** μ = 1080, σ = 20

5 a) μ = 40.0,   σ = 1.00   **b)** μ = 75.9,   σ = 2.36

c) μ = 120,   σ = 21.0   **d)** μ = 1081, σ = 20.0

Exercise 4.2

1 a) 0.9778 **b)** 0.8729 **c)** 0.8577 **d)** 0.5319

2 a) 0.9599 **b)** 0.9207 **c)** 0.7910 **d)** 0.9992

3 a) 1 − 0.8830 = 0.1170

b) 1 − 0.9015 = 0.0985

c) 1 − 0.9977 = 0.0023

d) 1 − 0.7486 = 0.2514

4 a) 1 − 0.9678 = 0.0322

b) 0.9357 − 0.8413 = 0.0944

c) 0.9015 − 0.5398 = 0.3617

d) 0.9987 − 0.9773 = 0.0214

5 a) $\Phi(1.31) - (1 - \Phi(1.7))$
$= 0.9049 - (1 - 0.9554) = 0.8603$

b) $\Phi(0.88) - (1 - \Phi(0.61))$
$= 0.8106 - (1 - 0.7291) = 0.5397$

c) $\Phi(1.18) - (1 - \Phi(1.1))$
$= 0.8810 - (1 - 0.8643) = 0.7453$

d) $\Phi(1.7) - \Phi(1.01)$
$= 0.9554 - 0.8438 = 0.1116$

e) $\Phi(1.91) - \Phi(1.07)$
$= 0.9719 - 0.8577 = 0.1142$

f) $\Phi(0.5) - (1 - \Phi(2.5))$
$= 0.6915 - (1 - 0.9938) = 0.6853$

6 a) $\dfrac{23.4 - 19.3}{4.8} = \dfrac{4.1}{4.8} = 0.854$

b) $\dfrac{17.6 - 19.3}{4.8} = \dfrac{-1.7}{4.8} = -0.354$

c) $\dfrac{19.3 - 19.3}{4.8} = \dfrac{0}{4.8} = 0$

d) $\dfrac{4.8 - 19.3}{4.8} = \dfrac{-14.5}{4.8} = 3.021$

7 a) $\dfrac{6.3 - 5.2}{2.2} = \dfrac{1.1}{2.2} = 0.5$

b) $\dfrac{3.8 - 5.2}{2.2} = \dfrac{-1.4}{2.2} = -0.636$

c) $\dfrac{0 - 5.2}{2.2} = \dfrac{-5.2}{2.2} = -2.364$

d) $\dfrac{15 - 5.2}{2.2} = \dfrac{9.8}{2.2} = 4.455$

8 a) $\dfrac{284 - 275}{8} = \dfrac{9}{8} = 1.125$

b) $\dfrac{255 - 275}{8} = \dfrac{-20}{8} = -2.5$

c) $\dfrac{290-275}{8}=\dfrac{15}{8}=1.875$

d) $\dfrac{250-275}{8}=\dfrac{-25}{8}=-3.125$

9 a) $\dfrac{800-810}{10}=\dfrac{-10}{10}=-1$ **b)** $\dfrac{825-810}{10}=\dfrac{15}{10}=1.5$

c) $\dfrac{816-810}{10}=\dfrac{6}{10}=0.6$ **d)** $\dfrac{806-810}{10}=\dfrac{-4}{10}=-0.4$

10 a) $\dfrac{185-120}{30}=\dfrac{65}{30}=2.167$

b) $\dfrac{72-120}{30}=\dfrac{-48}{30}=-1.6$

c) $\dfrac{96-120}{30}=\dfrac{-24}{30}=-0.8$

d) $\dfrac{163-120}{30}=\dfrac{43}{30}=1.43$

11 a) Since $\Phi(1.64)=0.95$, time waiting is
$14+1.64\times4=14+6.56=20.56$ min
Phone at 6:39 pm

b) Since $\Phi(2.33)=0.99$, time waiting is
$14+2.33\times4=14+9.32=23.32$ min
Phone at 6:37 pm

c) Since $\Phi(2.57)=0.995$, time waiting is
$14+2.57\times4=14+10.28=24.28$ min
Phone at 6:36 pm

d) Probability of 0.1 arriving after 7 pm is
probability 0.9 of arriving before
7 pm. Since $\Phi(1.28)=0.9$, time waiting is
$14+1.28\times4=14+5.12=19.12$ min
Phone at 6:41 pm

12 UQ: $\Phi(z)=0.75$ or $z=0.67$
LQ: $z=-0.67$ (by symmetry)
a) IQR $=(1120+0.67\times2.5)$
$-(1120-0.67\times2.5)$
$=2\times0.67\times2.5=3.4$ mm
b) IQR $=2\times0.67\times1.7=2.3$ mm

Exercise 4.3

1 Probability greater than $100.5°$ is
$P\left(z>\dfrac{100.5-98.3}{0.8}\right)=P(z>2.75)$
$=1-\Phi(2.75)=1-0.9970=0.0030$

2 a) Probability greater than 162 cm is
$P\left(z>\dfrac{162-155}{11.2}\right)=P(z>0.625)$
$=1-\Phi(0.625)=1-0.7324=0.2676$

b) Probability less than 158 cm is
$P\left(z<\dfrac{158-155}{11.2}\right)=P(z<0.268)$
$=\Phi(0.268)=0.6064$

c) Probability less than 146 cm is
$P\left(z<\dfrac{146-155}{11.2}\right)=P(z<-0.804)$
$=1-\Phi(0.804)=1-0.7881=0.2119$

d) $P(145<x<165)$
$=P\left(\dfrac{145-155}{11.2}<z<\dfrac{165-155}{11.2}\right)$
$=P(-0.893<z<0.893)$
$=\Phi(0.893)-(1-\Phi(0.893))$
$=2\times0.8141-1=0.6281$

3 a) Probability greater than 152 cm is
$P\left(z>\dfrac{152-149.3}{12.7}\right)=P(z>0.213)$
$=1-\Phi(0.213)=1-0.5832=0.4168$

b) Probability less than 154 cm is
$P\left(z<\dfrac{154-149.3}{12.7}\right)=P(z<0.370)$
$=\Phi(0.370)=0.6443$

c) Probability less than 145 cm is
$P\left(z<\dfrac{145-149.3}{12.7}\right)=P(z<-0.339)$
$=1-\Phi(0.339)=1-0.6331=0.3669$

d) Standardised measurement of
148 cm is $z=\dfrac{148-149.3}{12.7}=\dfrac{-1.3}{12.7}=-0.102$
Standardised measurement of
151 cm is $z=\dfrac{151-149.3}{12.7}=\dfrac{1.7}{12.7}=0.134$
Probability between 148 cm and 151 cm
is $\Phi(0.134)-(1-\Phi(0.102))=0.5517-$
$(1-0.5398)=0.0915$

4 a) $P(x<90)$ is $P\left(z<\dfrac{90-65}{20}\right)$
$=P(z<1.25)=0.8944$
b) $P(x>60)$ is $P\left(z>\dfrac{60-65}{20}\right)$
$=P(z>-0.25)=\Phi(0.25)=0.5987$

5 a) $P(x<60)$ is $P\left(z<\dfrac{60-48}{20}\right)$
$=P(z<0.6)=0.7257$
b) $P(30<x<60)=P(x<60)-P(x<30)$
$P(x<30)$ is $P\left(z<\dfrac{30-48}{20}\right)$
$=P(z<-0.9)=1-\Phi(0.9)=1-0.8159$
$P(30<x<60)=P(x<60)-P(x<30)$
$=0.7257-(1-0.8159)=0.5416$
c) $\Phi(1.28)=0.9\Rightarrow z=1.28$
$z=1.28=\dfrac{k-48}{20}$
$\Rightarrow k=48+20\times1.28=73.6$

6 a) $P(x < 205)$ is $P\left(z < \dfrac{205 - 184.5}{13.6}\right)$

$= P(z < 1.507) = 0.934 = 93.5\%$

b) $P(145 < x < 190)$ is

$P\left(\dfrac{145 - 184.5}{13.6} < z < \dfrac{190 - 184.5}{13.6}\right)$

$= P(-2.905 < z < 0.4044)$

$= \Phi(0.4044) - (1 - \Phi(2.905))$

$= 0.6554 - (1 - 0.9981) = 0.6535$

7 a) i) $P(x > 75)$ is $P\left(z > \dfrac{75 - 68}{13}\right)$

$= P(z > 0.538) = 1 - \Phi(0.538)$

$= 1 - 0.2946 = 0.7054$

ii) $P(58 < x < 72)$ is

$P\left(\dfrac{58 - 68}{13} < z < \dfrac{72 - 68}{13}\right)$

$= P(-0.7692 < z < 0.3077)$

$= \Phi(0.3077) - (1 - \Phi(0.7692))$

$= 0.6217 - (1 - 0.7794) = 0.4011$

b) $\Phi(1.28) = 0.9 \Rightarrow z = 1.28$

$z = 1.28 = \dfrac{p - 68}{13}$

$p = 68 + 13 \times 1.28 = 84.6$

8 $P(x < 25)$ is $P\left(z > \dfrac{25 - 31.6}{4.3}\right)$

$= P(z < -1.535) = 1 - \Phi(1.535)$

$= 1 - 0.9370 = 0.0630$

9 $P(\text{reject}) = P(x < 52) + P(x > 57)$

$= P\left(z < \dfrac{52 - 55}{1.5}\right) + P\left(z > \dfrac{57 - 55}{1.5}\right)$

$= [1 - \Phi(2)] + [1 - \Phi(1.333)]$

$= [1 - 0.9773] + [1 - 0.9082] = 0.1145$

No. reject nails $= 0.1145 \times 11\,000 = 1260$

No. good nails $= 11\,000 - 1260 = 9740$

Investigation

3 a) 0.121   **b)** 0.121

   c) 0.110   **d)** 0.091

Consolidation questions 4

1 a) $P(x > 21.5) = P\left(z > \dfrac{21.5 - 17.5}{2.5}\right)$

$= P(z > 1.6) = 1 - 0.9452 = 0.0548$

b) $1 - 0.127 = 0.873$

$\Phi(1.14) = 0.873 \Rightarrow z = 1.14$

$-1.14 = \dfrac{x - 17.5}{2.5}$

$\Rightarrow x = 17.5 - 2.5 \times 1.14 = 14.65$ cm

2 a) $P(x > 27) = P\left(z > \dfrac{27 - 24.9}{1.05}\right)$

$= P(z > 2) = 1 - \Phi(2) = 1 - 0.9772 = 0.0228$

b) $P(22 < x < 25)$ is

$P\left(\dfrac{22 - 22.8}{0.89} < z < \dfrac{25 - 22.8}{0.89}\right)$

$= P(-0.899 < z < 2.47)$

$= \Phi(2.47) - (1 - \Phi(0.899))$

$= 0.9932 - (1 - 0.8159) = 0.8091$

Percentage is 80.91

3 a) $P(H > 190) = P\left(z > \dfrac{190 - 178}{7}\right)$

$= P(z > 1.7143) = 1 - \Phi(1.7143)$

$= 1 - 0.9564 = 0.0436 = 4.36\%$

b) $P(147 < H < 203)$ is

$P\left(\dfrac{147 - 162}{6.4} < z < \dfrac{203 - 162}{6.4}\right)$

$= P(-2.344 < z < 6.406)$

$= \Phi(6.4066) - (1 - \Phi(2.344))$

$= 1 - (1 - 0.9904) = 0.9904 = 99.04\%$

4 a) $P(x < 200) = P\left(z > \dfrac{200 - 185}{10}\right)$

$= P(z < 1.5) = 0.9332$

b) $P(x > 175)$ is $P\left(Z > \dfrac{175 - 185}{10}\right)$

$= P(z > -1) = P(Z < 1) = 0.8413$

c) From above, probability is

a) $- (1 - $ **b)**$) = 0.7745$

5 a) i) $P(x < 145) = P\left(z > \dfrac{145 - 140}{2.5}\right)$

$= P(z < 2) = 0.9772$

ii) $P(138 < H < 142)$ is

$P\left(\dfrac{138 - 140}{2.5} < z < \dfrac{138 - 140}{2.5}\right)$

$= P(-0.8 < z < 0.8)$

$= \Phi(0.8) - (1 - \Phi(0.8))$

$= 0.7881 - (1 - 0.7881) = 0.5762$

b) $\Phi(-1.04) = 0.85 \Rightarrow z = -1.04$

(height exceeded by 85%)

$z = -1.04 = \dfrac{h - 140}{2.5}$

$h = 140 - 2.5 \times 1.04 = 137.4$ cm

Practice paper 1

1 a) $100 - 18.4 - 65.2 = 16.4$

b) $\dfrac{16.6}{100} \times 10605870 = 1\,760\,574$

or $1\,760\,000$

c) $209\,830 = 23.7\%$ of population

population $= \dfrac{209830}{23.7} \times 100 = 885\,359$

or $885\,000$

2 a) Mean is $\dfrac{1936}{100} = 19.36$ or 19.4

b) 15.70 or 15.7

3 a), cii)

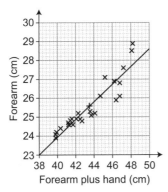

Forearm plus hand (cm)

b) i) 0.9268

ii) There is a high correlation between the two lengths.

c) i) $y = 0.46x + 5.45$

ii) For example, (0, 5.45) or (50, 28.6).

iii) This is the number of cm the forearm plus hand will grow for each extra 1 cm of forearm length.

iv) 49.0 cm

4 a)

	Men
19	1 1 7 8
18	3 6 8
17	0 3 3 7 9
16	1 3 4 5 6 7 7 8 8 9 9
15	8 9
14	

b) i) 169 cm

ii) $(183 + 18.6) \div 2 - (165 + 166) \div 2 = 19$ cm

d) Males have a higher mean and median height; the women have a smaller interquartile range, that is, they are more consistent in height.

5 a) i) $P(x > 182)$ is $P\left(z > \dfrac{182 - 152}{30}\right)$

$= P(z > 1) = 1 - \Phi(1)$

$= 1 - 0.8413 = 0.1587$

ii) $P(142 < x < 200)$ is

$P\left(\dfrac{142 - 152}{30} < z < \dfrac{200 - 152}{30}\right)$

$= P(-0.3333 < z < 1.6)$

$= \Phi(1.6) - (1 - \Phi(0.3333))$

$= 0.9452 - (1 - 0.6293) = 0.5745$

Practice paper 2

1 a) Mean = $239 \div 52 = 4.60$

Median = 4.5

Mode = 6

The data is almost bi-model with 4 and 6 births having similar frequencies.

b) Mean is better for state planning; median represents an 'average' week better

2 a) i)

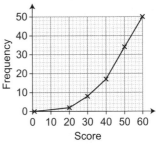

Score

ii) 45   **iii)** $52 - 35 = 17$

b) John's scores are, on average, lower than Sam's scores. John's scores are much more consistent than Sam's scores.

3 a)

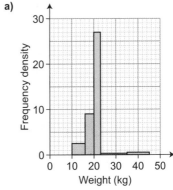

Weight (kg)

b) $2960.5 \div 146 = 20.28$ or 20.3 kg

c) 5.17 kg

4 a) i) $P(x > 182)$ is $P\left(z > \dfrac{182 - 174.3}{14.8}\right)$

$= P(z > 0.520) = 1 - \Phi(0.520)$

$= 1 - 0.6985 = 0.3015$

ii) $P(166 < x < 180)$ is

$= P\left(\dfrac{166 - 174.3}{14.8} < z < \dfrac{180 - 174.3}{14.8}\right)$

$= P(-0.561 < z < 0.385)$

$= \Phi(0.385) - (1 - \Phi(0.561))$

$= 0.6517 - (1 - 0.7123)$

$= 0.364$

5 a) i) $\bar{x} = 233.6 \div 12 = 19.47$ or 19.5 °C

$\bar{y} = 233.6 \div 12 = 8.25$ hours

ii) 0.8715

iii) $y = 0.3451x + 1.5315$

b) Use two points, for example, (19.47, 8.25) and (10, 4.98) to draw line

c) The average increase in the mean number hours of sunshine as the average temperature increases by one degree.

Standard normal distribution

The tabulated value is $\Phi(z)$, the probability that a random value from a standard normal distribution has a value less than or equal to z.

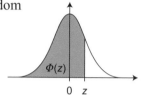

$\Phi(z)$

$0 \quad z$

z	0.00	0.01	0.02	0.03	0.04	0.05	0.06	0.07	0.08	0.09
0.0	0.5000	0.5040	0.5080	0.5120	0.5160	0.5199	0.5239	0.5279	0.5319	0.5359
0.1	0.5398	0.5438	0.5478	0.5517	0.5557	0.5596	0.5636	0.5675	0.5714	0.5753
0.2	0.5793	0.5832	0.5871	0.5910	0.5948	0.5987	0.6026	0.6064	0.6103	0.6141
0.3	0.6179	0.6217	0.6255	0.6293	0.6331	0.6368	0.6406	0.6443	0.6480	0.6517
0.4	0.6554	0.6591	0.6628	0.6664	0.6700	0.6736	0.6772	0.6808	0.6844	0.6879
0.5	0.6915	0.6950	0.6985	0.7019	0.7054	0.7088	0.7123	0.7157	0.7190	0.7224
0.6	0.7257	0.7291	0.7324	0.7357	0.7389	0.7422	0.7454	0.7486	0.7517	0.7549
0.7	0.7580	0.7611	0.7642	0.7673	0.7704	0.7734	0.7764	0.7794	0.7823	0.7852
0.8	0.7881	0.7910	0.7939	0.7967	0.7995	0.8023	0.8051	0.8078	0.8106	0.8133
0.9	0.8159	0.8186	0.8212	0.8238	0.8264	0.8289	0.8315	0.8340	0.8365	0.8389
1.0	0.8413	0.8438	0.8461	0.8485	0.8508	0.8531	0.8554	0.8577	0.8599	0.8621
1.1	0.8643	0.8665	0.8686	0.8708	0.8729	0.8749	0.8770	0.8790	0.8810	0.8830
1.2	0.8849	0.8869	0.8888	0.8907	0.8925	0.8944	0.8962	0.8980	0.8997	0.9015
1.3	0.9032	0.9049	0.9066	0.9082	0.9099	0.9115	0.9131	0.9147	0.9162	0.9177
1.4	0.9192	0.9207	0.9222	0.9236	0.9251	0.9265	0.9279	0.9292	0.9306	0.9319
1.5	0.9332	0.9345	0.9357	0.9370	0.9382	0.9394	0.9406	0.9418	0.9429	0.9441
1.6	0.9452	0.9463	0.9474	0.9484	0.9495	0.9505	0.9515	0.9525	0.9535	0.9545
1.7	0.9554	0.9564	0.9573	0.9582	0.9591	0.9599	0.9608	0.9616	0.9625	0.9633
1.8	0.9641	0.9649	0.9656	0.9664	0.9671	0.9678	0.9686	0.9693	0.9699	0.9706
1.9	0.9713	0.9719	0.9726	0.9732	0.9738	0.9744	0.9750	0.9756	0.9761	0.9767
2.0	0.9772	0.9778	0.9783	0.9788	0.9793	0.9798	0.9803	0.9808	0.9812	0.9817
2.1	0.9821	0.9826	0.9830	0.9834	0.9838	0.9842	0.9846	0.9850	0.9854	0.9857
2.2	0.9861	0.9864	0.9868	0.9871	0.9875	0.9878	0.9881	0.9884	0.9887	0.9890
2.3	0.9893	0.9896	0.9898	0.9901	0.9904	0.9906	0.9909	0.9911	0.9913	0.9916
2.4	0.9918	0.9920	0.9922	0.9925	0.9927	0.9929	0.9931	0.9932	0.9934	0.9936
2.5	0.9938	0.9940	0.9941	0.9943	0.9945	0.9946	0.9948	0.9949	0.9951	0.9952
2.6	0.9953	0.9955	0.9956	0.9957	0.9959	0.9960	0.9961	0.9962	0.9963	0.9964
2.7	0.9965	0.9966	0.9967	0.9968	0.9969	0.9970	0.9971	0.9972	0.9973	0.9974
2.8	0.9974	0.9975	0.9976	0.9977	0.9977	0.9978	0.9979	0.9979	0.9980	0.9981
2.9	0.9981	0.9982	0.9982	0.9983	0.9984	0.9984	0.9985	0.9985	0.9986	0.9986
3.0	0.9987	0.9987	0.9987	0.9988	0.9988	0.9989	0.9989	0.9989	0.9990	0.9990
3.1	0.9990	0.9991	0.9991	0.9991	0.9992	0.9992	0.9992	0.9992	0.9993	0.9993
3.2	0.9993	0.9993	0.9994	0.9994	0.9994	0.9994	0.9994	0.9995	0.9995	0.9995
3.3	0.9995	0.9995	0.9995	0.9996	0.9996	0.9996	0.9996	0.9996	0.9996	0.9997
3.4	0.9997	0.9997	0.9997	0.9997	0.9997	0.9997	0.9997	0.9997	0.9997	0.9998
3.5	0.9998	0.9998	0.9998	0.9998	0.9998	0.9998	0.9998	0.9998	0.9998	0.9998
3.6	0.9998	0.9998	0.9999	0.9999	0.9999	0.9999	0.9999	0.9999	0.9999	0.9999
3.7	0.9999	0.9999	0.9999	0.9999	0.9999	0.9999	0.9999	0.9999	0.9999	0.9999